BIRDS OF PREY

From the dawn of civilization, men have felt awe and fascination for the winged hunters of the skies, the birds of prey. The hawk's uncanny sight, the buzzard's high-altitude soaring, the vulture's sinister scavenging parties, the great eagle's screening descent and the owl's nocturnal hooting—all have been part of natural lore since ancient times.

Yet today, these magnificent birds are endangered in many regions of the world. Sadly, man himself must accept the blame for their plight. Thoughtlessly, he has destroyed the birds' natural habitats, hunted them to near extinction and introduced toxic pesticides into their food chains. If we fail to save these majestic creatures, our loss will be more than that of their beauty alone, for they are mankind's true allies against the rodents and other pests that take a heavy toll on agricultural products.

This authoritative book speaks of all the world's living birds of prey. It presents handsome color plates of many species, at the same time discussing the birds' life cycles, hunting and nesting behavior, and geographic ranges. The text also describes how to train these birds for the sport of falconry. Although chiefly written for the layman, the professional ornithologist may be drawn to the sections on feeding and sexual dimorphism—where new theories and new discoveries are discussed.

A
GROSSET
ALL-COLOR GUIDE

BIRDS OF PREY

BY GLENYS AND DEREK LLOYD

Illustrated by Ken Lilly

GROSSET & DUNLAP
A NATIONAL GENERAL COMPANY
Publishers • New York

THE GROSSET ALL-COLOR GUIDE SERIES
SUPERVISING EDITOR ... GEORG ZAPPLER

Board of Consultants

CONTENTS

4 Introduction

6 Life habits

22 Special Characteristics

32 Hunting and feeding

44 Sexual dimorphism

48 Nesting and training the young

56 Keeping birds of prey

68 Systematic list of hawklike birds and owls

156 Books to read

156 Places to visit

157 Index

California Condor

Red-thighed Falconet

INTRODUCTION

Some birds live by killing and eating other animals. These are the hunters of the bird world. There are other birds that eat the flesh of dead animals—the scavengers. These renders of meat fall into two main groups or orders: the hawklike species, including both hunters and scavengers; and the owls, mostly night-flying raptors.

Hawklike birds of prey are members of the order Falconiformes, which includes the buzzards, eagles, falcons, harriers, hawks and vultures. Most authorities identify about 290 species of Falconiformes, although some recognize only around 270. The latter hold that certain closely related forms are varieties of the same species rather than distinct species.

Approximately 130 different owls belong to the order Strigiformes. The owls are more like one another in anatomy and habits than are the hawklike species. Still owls differ greatly in size. The Elf Owl, for instance, weighs a few ounces,

4

Great
Eagle Owl

Elf Owl

while the Great Eagle Owl is nearly as large as the Golden Eagle.

People mistakenly give the name *eagle* to many large birds of prey. Sea eagles are really very large kites. Many other so-called eagles are related to buzzards and harriers. Several of the true eagles are actually quite small.

By the same token, American vultures may not necessarily be related to other hawklike birds but may simply be scavengers that evolved on lines similar to the Old World vultures.

The Secretary Bird and the Fish-eating Osprey have also puzzled ornithologists. But probably they are correctly included in the order Falconiformes. Of the rest, the falcons are most distinct—with a number of intriguing anatomical specializations.

Most people think of birds of prey as eaters of warm-blooded animals. In fact, some eat a wide variety of cold-blooded creatures, and others are partly vegetarian.

Many raptorial birds are very small. Certain pygmy falcons are barely larger than a sparrow, but they are more lethal killers, actually, than are the giant condors, with their ten-foot wing span, for the small falcons devour birds far larger than themselves.

5

LIFE AND HABITS

Life and Death

Most birds of prey—in common with other birds—never see their first birthday. In many species, it is estimated that as many as three-quarters of the young which hatch die during their first year. Failure to find suitable unoccupied territory and inexperience are the main causes of mortality. Also, many young get shot, because at an early age their awareness of danger is relatively undeveloped.

Inexperience at hunting causes young birds to attack unsuitable quarry. Hence they often become tired after a long fruitless chase and collide with a tree or a rock. Most birds of prey found injured are first-year birds, and an injured fledgling has little chance of survival since it has no mate to hunt for it. Young birds often choose unfavorable places for roosting and thus may be killed by other predators during the night. They may be attacked by large owls, if they are small species, or, if large birds, fall victim to marauders, such as

Broken and worn claws   Bumble foot

6

leopards and wolverines. Many birds are also killed or badly weakened by the low temperatures of winter or by gale-force winds.

Yet, once an individual survives its first year, it has mastered all the tricks of survival that should allow it to reach a ripe old age—barring accident or disease.

Although disease is not a common cause of death, the bird's feet are vulnerable to injuries that can have fatal consequences. As killing weapons, great strain is put upon the claws, often resulting in cuts or splits in the skin through which infection enters and causes swelling that makes the feet useless. The birds appear prone to kidney infections. Respiratory disease, pneumonia in particular, can afflict those in poor physical condition or the very old. Broken or twisted claws can lead to death, since any defect in the talons limits the bird's prowess in capturing and killing quarry. Also, beaks become deformed in old age, or grow too large and cumbersome for the act of tearing and eating the prey's flesh.

Except in a few species, fights to the death over territory

Some beak deformities

or for mates are very rare. This should not be surprising. For these birds, given their lethal armament, would have long-since eliminated themselves from the animal kingdom if they regularly engaged in intraspecies combat. Their strong talons have proved a deterrant to war.

In recent years, a new threat has been posed to the Falconiformes and the owls: man's widespread use of insecticides. The chemicals, sprayed on seeds, crops and trees, are absorbed by the smaller plant-eating creatures on which the winged hunter must prey to survive. When the predator consumes a large number of contaminated animals, pesticide-residues in its own tissues build up—eventually reaching the point where the bird dies from poisoning or, equally tragic, becomes sterile because of the chemical side-effects of the poisons.

If a bird of prey can escape all the above mentioned pitfalls, it may live to be quite old. Condors and the bigger vultures are on record as living to sixty years. The largest owls may live from forty to sixty years, also. The bigger eagles and carrion hawks have potential life spans of thirty to forty years, while Bateleurs seem exceptionally long living eagles—two in captivity attaining forty-five and fifty-five years. Small eagles, large hawks, buzzards and falcons, as well as medium-sized owls, reach up to thirty years, with an occasional bird surpassing this age. Small hawks and falcons do not normally exceed fifteen years, but a few small owls live up to twenty years.

Most of the above life spans are drawn from birds kept in captivity. At death, examination reveals that their tissues resemble those of humans aged seventy to ninety. The chart on the opposite page shows some of the maximum ages recorded for captive birds of prey.

Longevity Chart
Maximum age recorded

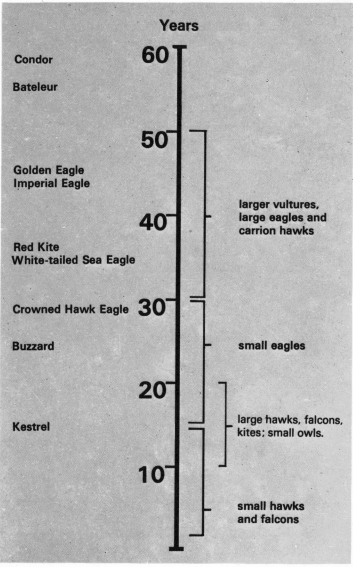

Years

	Years	
	60	
Condor		
Bateleur		
	50	larger vultures, large eagles and carrion hawks
Golden Eagle Imperial Eagle	40	
Red Kite White-tailed Sea Eagle		
Crowned Hawk Eagle	30	
Buzzard		small eagles
	20	large hawks, falcons, kites; small owls.
Kestrel		
	10	small hawks and falcons

Territory

Many birds of prey are gregarious, especially those that live on carrion, fish or insects. Such birds often live in scattered colonies. Some go hunting in groups, particularly those that catch insects in mid-air.

The majority of the Falconiformes and almost all owls, however, live in pairs on a defined territory or home range of their own. An ideal territory has certain basic characteristics: it provides sufficient food for the pair the year round—with an extra abundance at the peak of the season to raise a brood of young; it contains nesting sites and roosting places that afford protection from the wind in colder climates and from human and animal predators.

While the territories of most birds of prey vary between one and ten square miles, certain species can get along with less and other species need more. For example, a pair of small owls in an area harboring a heavy mouse population may require as little as fifty acres. At the other extreme, Africa's Verreaux's Eagle may need 250 square miles or more. This eagle specializes in catching the elusive rock hyraxes, which live in colonies on isolated, rocky hills. The appropriate hillsides may be scattered over vast regions of eastern and southern Africa. The Verreaux's Eagle will then be force to navigate far and wide to feed itself and its mate, as well as a young bird when it has bred successfully.

Large forest eagles often need as much room as the Verreaux's species. Seldom, in fact, are the nests of the larger species, such as the Harpy and the Crowned Eagle, located less than ten miles apart—giving each pair approximately one hundred square miles of exclusive range. Of course, the variety of prey taken by a bird has a bearing on how much territory it needs. A good example is the Great Horned Owl. Able to exist on a broad menu of mammals and birds, it may require only a square mile or two in area. Another exception to hard and fast territorial rules is provided by species such as the harriers and the short-eared owls. Although they defend exclusive preserves during the breeding season, at other times of year they tend to congregate in communal roosts from which they fly off in different directions to hunt. In the winter months in western Scotland, the Golden Eagle patrolling one hundred square miles of range, may still be forced to resort to sheep and deer carrion to survive.

Although birds may patrol large territories, they sometimes

Verreaux's Eagle in typical territory.

nest quite near to each other. A forst surrounded by open country or a wooded valley in hilly terrain often holds two or more nests, perhaps only a few hundred yards apart. The birds range away from their nests in different directions. Often such territory goes undefended. At other times, though, an area between territories is visited by the neighboring pairs of birds, some of which may attempt to hold a part of the area for themselves for a temporary period.

Usually the area around the nest is most strongly defended, although when birds have eggs or young they may become less active so as not to reveal the site of the nest to other birds or predators. The nesting area will be defended against any large bird that poses a threat to it, such as other birds of prey, owls, crows, or ravens.

Those species that migrate obviously give up their claims to the territories and the hunting areas they have held during the breeding season. Many of them take over a territory in their new wintering areas. But it is intended only as a source of food, not as a mating ground.

Among those birds of prey that do not migrate from their breeding areas in autumn, a number of things may happen after the young have left the nest. Sometimes the parent pair will stay in the same place or territory, not bothering to defend it as strongly as they did while breeding. Other birds wander over a very much larger area that may include the recently held territories of other pairs of their own species. They may even live semi-gregariously with these pairs.

Often, birds of prey will defend their territory, after breeding, against members of their own species, as well as against other species that hunt in a manner similar to themselves or take the same prey and are, therefore, competition to them.

Owls generally defend their territory throughout the year. They can be very aggressive towards intruders, either during the breeding season or when food is scarce.

Saw-whet Owl roosting in top of young fir tree—background shows typical territory of a small owl.

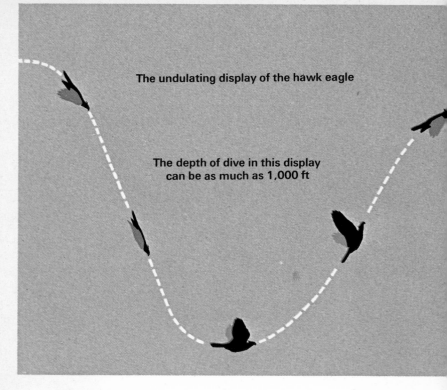

The undulating display of the hawk eagle

The depth of dive in this display can be as much as 1,000 ft

Displays

On sighting another bird of its own species or a species that poses a threat to its eggs or young, one or both of the territory owners sets off towards it in direct powerful flight. The meaning of this 'threat flight' is at once clear to the intruding bird, which normally turns and flies back. If the intruder is merely trying to cross the range of its neighbors, it tries to avoid them by changing direction and flying at full speed. If caught, a running fight may ensue. The intruder tries to avoid the blows of its pursuers. Although buffeted, it is unlikely to sustain real injury as neither side wants a really serious encounter. On reaching the boundary of the range, the aggressive owners usually turn for home or soar up in circles, watching to make sure that the intruder does not return.

Other raptors, such as crows and ravens, will be attacked if they enter the nesting area. Similarly these birds will attack should a hawklike bird or owl venture into their nesting territory. Small birds of prey position themselves

above and behind a larger one, crossing their territory. By means of harassment, darting, screaming and other tactics, they try to move it on. The intruder generally accelerates to escape and in so doing leaves the nesting area.

In good weather, birds of prey frequently soar along the edges of their territory. This action marks out to other birds of the same species the area the owners regard as their own.

Short-winged forest eagles are not adept at soaring for very long periods. So these birds have evolved spectacular displays—circling upward, then diving to pick up speed, suddenly at the bottom of the dive shooting upward on the momentum gained. The process is repeated, the bird crossing its territory in a series of undulations, emitting a loud piping call, audible for miles. Hence, any other eagle nearby can hear that the stretch of forest is claimed

A similarly spectacular display is performed to impress the bird's mate. The bird of prey dives at a tremendous speed, just missing its partner which may be perched or flying slowly. Or the bird may perform daring flight movements, such as corkscrews and loops, which look marvelous to human observers and probably also to other birds. A pair of Bald Eagles sometimes joins feet high in the air, then falls earthward executing graceful cartwheels.

Bald Eagles spiraling with claws interlocked

Arctic owls, whose courtship takes place by the light of the midnight sun, often give aerial displays. To most owls such acrobatics would be pointless, since birds in the air at night are almost invisible. Call notes figure in owls' displays, as well as bowing, wing clapping, mutual preening and bill touching, and courtship feeding (normally it is the male that brings the food). Such behavior is an important part of courtship for many of the birds of prey, particularly the smaller falcons. Mutual preening is commonplace among paired birds of prey. Female birds may beg

Threat display of Spotted Eagle Owl

food from the male in the manner of a young bird begging from its parent, often with chick-like noises.

Many owls puff out their feathers to impress their partners during courtship. The same display also shows aggression, making the bird appear much larger than it really is. Bill snapping is part of another display, in which the wings are opened and held forward. At the same time the owl may shuffle from one foot to the other, giving the impression of ferocity.

Many of the forest birds of prey possess a crest, which they raise and expand to show aggression. The wings, if opened, are usually held with the undersides toward the intruder; the bird may lean back on its tail, making it possible to lash out with both feet, in the event of attack. Often a lot of noises are made at this time, to inform the mate that an aggressor is present. On the other hand, hawk-like birds and owls brooding eggs or young, if they see a large intruder, first crouch low and keep completely still—until approached within a yard or two. Chicks do not develop this habit until quite late. Thus they often give the nest site away through calling or moving.

Migration

Most of the hawklike birds and owls that summer in areas with very cold winters migrate seasonally to a warmer climate. The main reason for this is the wintertime shortage of food. In winter many of the northern mammals hibernate while others live under the snow. Most small birds are gone, and reptiles, amphibians and insects are hidden away. Fish are under the ice. Certain tropical birds of prey also migrate between areas, especially in regions affected by periods of rain or drought.

In Scandinavia most of the birds of prey leave for the winter. Falsterbo, near the southern tip of Sweden, is a place where various migration routes converge. Thousands of Common and Rough-legged Buzzards, Honey Buzzards, Kestrels and Sparrow Hawks, and various eagles, Goshawks, and Ospreys may be seen on a single day if the weather is suitable for migration (dry and sunny with a fresh breeze).

Many of the eastern European birds of prey leave via the Bosphorus, straits at the mouth of the Black Sea. Imperial, Steppe, Lesser and Greater Spotted Eagles may all be seen, as well as Short-toed, Booted and White-tailed Eagles, as they cross the narrow waters. Peregrines, Sakers, Lanners, Lesser Kestrels and Red-footed Falcons go with them. With the exception of the harriers and certain falcons, the Falconiformes find traveling across wide stretches of water difficult, because of the absence of warm updrafts on which they depend to gain height. It is not surprising, therefore, to find that the narrow Strait of Gibraltar is the place where most western European migrants cross into Africa (although some go no farther south than Spain).

In Asia, apart from Gyr Falcons and Golden Eagles, most raptors migrate to India, southeast Asia and the Malay Archipelago. Hobbys, Peregrines and Steppe Eagles cross the Himalayas in autumn and return in spring. Two small hawks of eastern Asia—the Chinese Goshawk and the Rufous-winged Buzzard—migrate as far as New Guinea. The greatest Old World migrant is the Eastern Red-footed Falcon. Breeding in northeast China, it winters in Rhodesia in central Africa. No one knows for certain whether after passing over India the Eastern Red-Foots fly across the

Autumn migration in Old World

* observation points
  general drift
  broad front migration
  concentrated migration
  Red-footed Falcon (eastern race)

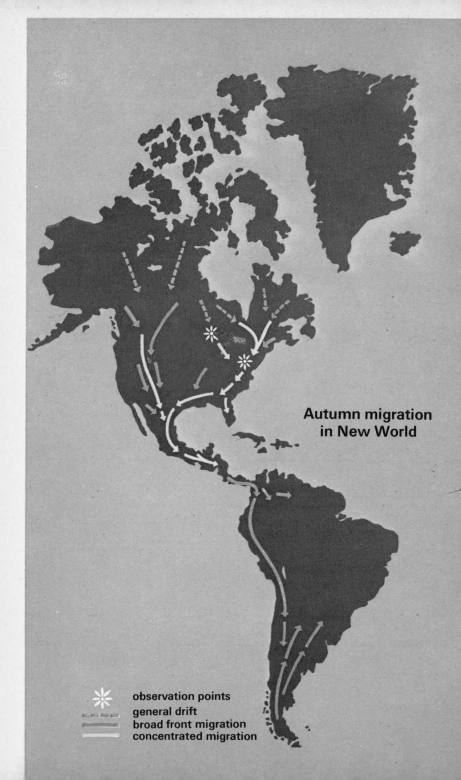

**Autumn migration
in New World**

✳   observation points
        general drift
        broad front migration
        concentrated migration

Indian Ocean to reach Rhodesia. They have not been seen in flight anywhere between India and Kenya. Perhaps they do follow a transoceanic route, for they are known to be extremely fat before their departure, a condition common to many birds which migrate across large areas where food is unobtainable.

Both Long-eared and Short-eared Owls—long-winged species—migrate considerable distances. But most other owls are not so equipped for sustained flight. Condemned by nature to endure the long cold winter, they take refuge in sheltered woodlands and valleys. Their winter plumage is extremely thick—three quarters of what one sees of a Great Gray Owl is feathers—and their feet are also well feathered. Their habit of roosting in holes helps keep them warm in winter. Even so, food is hard to find, and many perish.

In North America, Snowy Owls and most hawklike birds move south in hard winters. In the east, the Appalachian range forms one of the main routes. At places such as Hawk Mountain, in Pennsylvania, up to 20,000 birds are seen during the year. Broad-winged and Red-tailed Buzzards and Sharp-shinned Hawks are the most numerous species; Turkey Vultures, Ospreys, Cooper's, Goshawks, Peregrines and Merlins may also be seen.

The Great Lakes form a barrier to hawk migration. Thousands of birds thus fly around the western end of Lake Superior and south along the shores of Lake Michigan. The Broad-winged Hawk of eastern North America migrates as far south as western Brazil and Peru—some 4,000 miles. More impressive, Swainson's Buzzard makes a round trip of up to 17,000 miles every winter—from the Rocky Mountains to and from the pampas of Argentina. Some species breeding in southern Argentina, notably the Aplomado Falcon and the Cinereous Harrier, migrate north in the southern-hemispheric winter. Some of Argentina's insect eating species, such as the Swallow-tailed and Plumbeous Kites, move northward into Brazil in the cooler weather, just as their opposite numbers in the United States and Mexico go south into Central America during the northern winter.

SPECIAL CHARACTERISTICS

Wings and Tails

A bird of prey must use its wings to reach its food. It may be a case of long hours of soaring observation to find a dead animal in a large expanse of open country, or the sprinter's task of catching another bird flying at 80 miles an hour.

Finding a wide variety of foods involves very different activities. Thus, birds of prey have evolved various types of wings, according to the type of hunting they specialize in.

A bird, such as a vulture, that searches endlessly for dead animals will often need to fly 200 or more miles in a day. Flying, especially flapping flight, can consume a great deal of energy. Hence, vultures have developed very long, broad

Lanner Falcon

Himalayan Griffon

wings. These enable them to soar easily and then glide for great distances with very little flapping. The big disadvantage of such large wings is that they make taking off and landing cumbersome, nor are they effective for rapid acceleration. Since most vultures do not have to catch their food, the advantages obviously outweigh the disadvantages. In contrast to huge wings, vultures have small tails. The tail, which in birds of prey is composed of twelve or occasionally fourteen feathers, acts as a rudder. Since vultures seldom need to turn quickly, they need only a small tail.

Large eagles also often eat carrion but they take live prey as well. Thus, they have rather shorter, narrower wings than do vultures. They have a much larger, stronger tail. These adaptations enable them to land and turn quickly when seizing prey moving on the ground.

Some of the kites have long narrow wings and are accomplished at soaring and gliding. They are, however, very light birds. Heavier, narrow-winged birds cannot soar except in ideal weather conditions.

The harriers, although they possess fairly long wings and are lightly built, seldom soar. Rather they glide low over open country and marshland. A few flaps followed by a glide allows them to cruise along silently and take their prey by surprise.

Shikra, an
Asiatic goshawk

Montagu's Harrier

Hawk-owl

Many diurnal hunters, from tiny hawks to the largest eagles, exploit forests and wooded country and are adapted for catching the various birds and mammals that live there. They have evolved short, broad wings and long tails. With this combination they are able to fly rapidly among the trees and to turn very sharply as the prey—it may be anything from a small bird (in the case of a hawk) to a monkey (in the case of a large eagle)—tries to reach cover.

Most of the falcons possess narrow wings, the heavier ones having wings broader at the base, which let them soar effectively. Long, narrow-tipped wings enable a bird to fly very quickly in pursuit of prey. When hunting other birds, falcons usually soar above their prey and then dive. Using the speed gained in the dive, they overtake their victims. This is called 'stooping.' The Peregrine Falcon is particularly fond of stooping its victims at an incredible speed in an almost vertical dive, knocking them out of the sky with its talons.

Since hawklike birds are seen most often when they are soaring high in the sky, identification can be extremely difficult. The precise shape and pattern of the wing is important in distinguishing between species, and so are the length, shape and pattern of the tail. Slight variations in underwing markings and wing shape enable the experienced observer to identify many species that to the beginner are indistinguishable. The angle at which the wings are held may also help to identify a particular bird of prey.

24

Little Owl

Short-eared Owl

Owls' wings are much less variable in shape than are those of the Falconiformes. Owls do not search for carrion from high altitudes (since this would be impractical in the dark). Hence none has unusually long, broad wings.

Barn owls and marsh owls hunt over open country in the way that harriers do, and have long, narrow harrier-like wings. Some of the hawk owls have long, strong tails reminiscent of hawks, which enable them to turn sharply while pursuing small birds in flight. But most owls have rather short wings and tails. For predatory birds they are not particularly maneuverable or fast. This is no disadvantage, however, for their feathers give them a most important adaption for night hunting—silent flight. Their plumage, including all their flight feathers, is soft and pliable; soft feathers drawn quickly through the air produce no sound.

Sparrow Hawk with
House Sparrow

Feet

In most birds, feet are simply for walking, hopping or supporting the bird's weight while it is at rest. But in the hawklike birds and the owls, feet have evolved another more specialized purpose: that of weapons. Some of the predators also use their beaks to help in killing their quarry, but in nearly all cases the feet are the main weapons and are often, therefore, highly developed.

Except for some of the fish-eaters, birds of prey have three toes pointing forward and one toe pointing backward. The hind toe and the inside toe are generally stronger than the others, possessing thicker and longer claws. Most birds of prey can exert an extremely powerful thumb and forefinger grip with these two toes. The claws can be driven straight into a vulnerable spot on the prey, or used to crush the creature. With powerful movements of its legs, the predator can also dislocate the prey's neck; most of the larger hawks, buzzards and eagles kill by this method. Their middle and outer toes are generally used only to balance the foot while the bird is perching or walking.

Some of the hawks and falcons that specialize in catching birds have evolved a very long middle toe. This helps the

26

bird to bind to its prey by giving its foot a much wider grip. Without it, if the prey turned sharply in flight just as the hawk struck, the hawk's inside claws alone would not be able to secure a grip and the victim would escape.

Birds of prey that kill poisonous snakes have very short toes, giving them a very strong, firm grip from which the prey cannot wriggle free. Generally, the vultures do not have strong inside toes. When tearing at a carcass, the vulture puts its weight on the inside claw, which is larger than but not as powerfully muscled as the other toes. In the American vultures, the hind claw has become very small and is of little use. Most vultures have

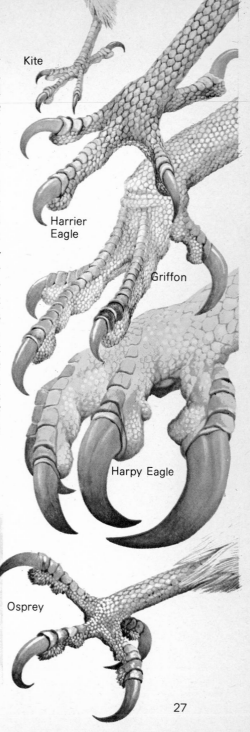

Kite

Harrier Eagle

Griffon

Harpy Eagle

Osprey

27

feet somewhat like a chicken's that enable them to run quickly on the ground, either around a carcass, or when taking off after a heavy meal. Kites, which generally feed on small prey or scavenge, have feet as unspecialized for killing as those of vultures.

The Osprey and the Gray-headed and Lesser Fishing Eagles possess two claws facing forward and two facing backward. These birds live mainly by catching fish using both feet together so that the fish is held with four claws on each side. Spine-like scales on their toes are a further adaptation for holding the slippery prey.

The prey-seizing adaptation in which two toes face forward and two face backward is also found in all the owls. Owls' feet are not as strong as the feet of the more rapacious birds of prey, but their claws are often sharper. Generally, owls use all four claws as offensive weapons and rarely, if ever, dismember their victims.

Snowy Owl and lemming

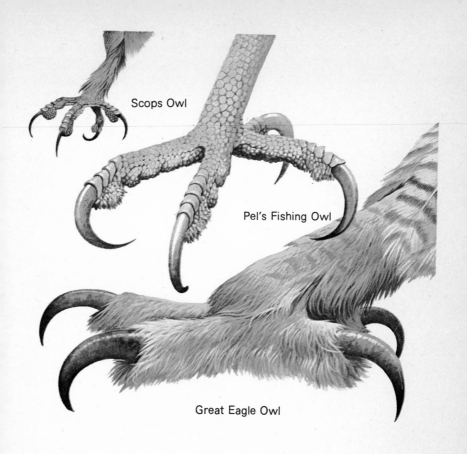

Scops Owl

Pel's Fishing Owl

Great Eagle Owl

In contrast to the other predatory birds, most owls have feathered legs and feet. However, the owls that catch fish share with the hawklike birds the adaptation of bared lower legs and feet. Probably, this is because the legs get wet when the birds are hunting. Moreover, fish scales are difficult to remove from feathers. Thus, this adaptation fits well with these owls' way of life. They also have spine-like scales on their toes, similar in function to those of fish-eating Falconiformes.

The feet of most hawklike birds are bloodstained and messy after feeding, as they usually dismember their victims. Feet bare of feathers are therefore an advantage since they can be easily cleaned. In contrast, most owls swallow their prey whole. As a result, foot feathers are not a disadvantage.

Sociable Vulture

Egyptian Vulture

Beaks

The main function of the beak of a bird of prey is to rip its food into pieces which it can swallow. The beak cannot be used to peck, as it can in most birds, because it is the wrong shape. A Golden Eagle has a typically strong, tearing beak. The bird bites so that the hook of the bill is forced into the flesh; then, with both inner claws planted firmly in the prey, the eagle strains back, tearing off a piece of flesh as it does so. The piece is then swallowed and the process repeated.

The beaks of Snake Eagles are generally smaller than those of other eagles. They swallow snakes whole if possible and do not need to do much tearing. But they have very strong jaw muscles and can bite much harder than other eagles. They are able to bite straight through the head of a snake once they have secured a grip near the head with their talons.

Vultures have a large variety in the sizes and shapes of their beaks. The huge bill of the Sociable Vulture is suitable for tearing off and gulping down huge pieces of muscle. At the other extreme, the small Egyptian Vulture, usually arriving last at the carcass, has a long slender bill, ideal for extracting the small pieces of flesh from between bones which would be overlooked by the larger vultures.

The falcons often use their bills to assist in killing. A falcon has a tooth-like incision in its upper mandible that fits into a notch in the lower mandible and is used to sever the bones at the back of the victim's neck. Some of the smaller kites have two such tooth-like incisions in the upper mandible that are

Golden Eagle

Great
Eagle Owl

probably an adaptation for dismembering large insects which are held in the foot.

One of the strangest beaks is possessed by the Bat Hawk of Asia and Africa. This hawk hunts at dusk, catching bats and insects in the air with its talons. It transfers the catch to its mouth and while still on the wing, swallows it whole. The bill has a ridge along the top of the upper mandible and an enormous gape like that of the nightjars.

Generally, owls have small, neat beaks. Since they swallow much of their prey whole, none has developed a very large beak for tearing flesh. As a result, large owls with big prey take much longer to feed than do the Falconiformes. An interesting habit of owls is that they are able to signal aggression by clacking their bills loudly. The lower mandible is extended over the hook of the upper, and then drawn back to clap against the upper mandible.

Peregrine Falcon

Cuckoo Falcon

HUNTING AND FEEDING

Hunting Methods

Hunting is a very specialized activity. If the hunter merely flew after another animal hoping to catch it, it would seldom achieve anything except exhaustion. Hunting is a difficult art; consequently a large percentage of young birds never become proficient hunters and die during their first few months of independence.

When hunting, the experienced raptor seeks prey that it can catch without using maximum effort. It therefore generally looks for quarry smaller than itself. If forced to prey on fast moving birds or large mammals, it usually seeks an individual that is sick or has become separated from its flock. Birds of prey are not capable of hunting at maximum effort every day, just as no man can always work at his peak level. When times are hard and the birds or their young are very hun-

Mountain Hawk Eagle above
musk deer

32

Kestrel or Sparrow Hawk hovering

gry, many species are capable of killing animals larger and stronger than themselves.

Vultures hunt for dead animals. They fly at great heights from which they cannot always tell whether an animal is dead or not. So they watch other carrion-eaters over a wide area, including crows, kites, jackals, hyenas and large carnivores. If a vulture's interest is aroused by something going on below, it will circle lower. This movement will be seen by vultures a mile or so away on each side of it. If food is definitely available, it will begin to lose height quickly. The birds patrolling within sight will recognize the significance of this descent and will set their own wings into a long fast glide toward the spot the first bird is making for. Vultures father away, seeing their neighbors descending, will do likewise. Within minutes, therefore, many vultures will be arriving at the carcass from all directions.

A common method of hunting used by many birds is a sort of ambush, which ornithologists call 'still' hunting. A bird of prey selects a concealed vantage point, usually a tree with a command of the ground below. Any mammal or ground-feeding bird that turns its back to the tree becomes vulnerable. This method sounds easy, but skilled timing is essential. A bird diving too fast or too steeply at its prey will need to brake hard before hitting its quarry. This action may create enough noise to cause the victim to bolt. To brake and turn together is impossible, and the attack will be unsuccessful.

Small rodents, snakes, and lizards living in flat, open grassland cannot be hunted from a perch. To catch such prey, birds have evolved the ability to hover. They fly slowly into the wind with wings beating forward and the tail depressed and fanned.

From a stationary overhead position, the birds can detect any small movement in the grass. Usually they drop to about fifty feet, hovering there again before finally plunging feet first onto the prey. The best known European bird of prey, the Kestrel, uses this method of hunting with excellent results.

Another method of hunting over flat country is that used by long-winged, lightweight birds of prey. They glide very low over the ground. Every few seconds they make a few wing flaps to maintain height. Any prey feeding on the ground with its back to the predator may be surprised or be too slow in making for cover to avoid capture. Harriers are typcial birds of prey that use this method of hunting. They patrol the ground very carefully and patiently, gliding low on wings held in a shallow "V", and pounce on any unsuspecting prey. The Marsh Harrier, which hunts over reed beds, often seems to fall clumsily into the reeds when capturing prey. Some long-winged owls, like the short-eared species, often hunt over open marshland in a similar manner for mice and other small rodents.

Gyr Falcon stooping at Ptarmigan

A fast low-flying dash is employed by many birds of prey. Those hunting in wooded country have short wings and long tails that enable them to turn rapidly. They sight their prey, such as a squirrel, only when close to it. The quarry usually sights them at the same moment and rushes for the nearest cover. The European Sparrow Hawk, a typical short-winged hawk, hunter of small birds in woods or alongside hedgerows, flies swiftly along a hedge, first on one side then on the other, prepared to pounce on an unsuspecting victim. Short wings, although they let a bird accelerate very quickly, are ineffectual for sustained flight. Birds hunting by means of the dash over open country have long wings to enable them to fly fast for long distances.

High soaring flight is used by some birds to scout for prey. From high in the air, the quarry is watched until it moves into a vulnerable position away from cover. It may never do so, in which case the hunter will have wasted its time. But should it move into an open field or a clearing, the bird of prey sets off in a rapid glide toward it. After a rapid descent, the bird brakes hard with wings and tail before striking, giving the quarry a chance to escape. But if the attacker has timed his move cor-

Verreaux's Eagle and Hyrax

Little Owl and wood mouse

rectly the prey will be far enough from cover so that it cannot reach it. Some eagles that live in open country, including the Golden Eagle and the African Martial Eagle, often use this method of hunting. From a high soaring position certain birds of prey catch other birds flying across open country. Following a fast-dive, the hunter overtakes the quarry before it can reach cover. Many birds of prey use more than one hunting strategy.

With few exceptions, owls are still hunters or low-level gliders hunting in open country. As is well known, they have remarkably sharp eyesight at night, but they have an even more effective aid for nocturnal hunting: three-dimensional hearing. Owls possess facial discs shaped to trap sound waves, as well as ears located in different positions on each side of the head that allow them to judge the distance and direction from which a sound originates. When hunting on dark moonless nights, most owls are able to locate and strike their quarry by sound alone. But if the prey suddenly becomes stationary and hence silent, then the owl utilizes its sharp vision. Owls have an added advantage in that most of their prey cannot see them. Their silent flight and the darkness make them undetectable from the ground.

Owls also have the ability to rotate their heads nearly in a full circle. As a result, they can locate sounds coming from any direction without changing position.

European Eagle Owl with hedgehog

White-headed Falconet (*left*) and Indian Black Vulture with distended crops

Food

Not surprisingly, a pygmy falcon requires only about one ounce of food a day, while a giant condor needs about one pound.

Yet, smaller birds eat far more food in comparison to their size. For instance, pygmy falcons actually eat the equivalent of about half its body weight in a single day. Generally, this is because an animal loses body heat through its skin, which is the surface of its body. Surface is larger in proportion to volume in small creatures. Hence, little animals need more food to maintain body temperature than large ones. This increased requirement necessitates greater activity in quest of food, and this activity itself adds to the need. This is seen in the feeding behavior of the aforementioned birds. While pygmy falcons are constant, frenetic hunters, the condors—requiring only three to four percent of their body weight in food daily—may feed only twice a week.

Indeed, any large bird that has eaten well previously can readily survive one week, or two, or more of famine. A Steller's Sea Eagle at the London Zoo that had become overweight voluntarily fasted for six weeks. The smallest raptors, by contrast, can go without food only for a day or two.

The following table shows the body weights and food requirements of typical species.

	Weight of Bird	Weekly Food Consumption
Red-thighed Falconet	1¾ oz.	6 oz.
Spix Scops Owl	4 oz.	7½ oz.
American Sparrow Hawk	4 oz.	8½ oz.
European Sparrow Hawk	8 oz.	10 oz.
Tawny Owl	1 lb.	12 oz.
Peregrine Falcon	1 lb. 11 oz.	1 lb. 4 oz.
European Buzzard	2 lb. 2 oz.	1 lb. 4 oz.
Short-toed Eagle	4 lb. 6 oz.	1 lb. 13 oz.
Great Eagle Owl	6 lb.	2 lb. 2 oz.
Golden Eagle	8 lb. 4 oz.	3 lb. 3 oz.
Lammergeyer	12 lb. 8 oz.	4 lb.
Andean Condor	25 lb.	6 lb. 12 oz.

Most birds must kill prey weighing appreciably more than the food weight indicated in the table, unless they swallow their prey whole. The amount of a carcass left uneaten varies according to the species of predator, how hungry it is, and the edibility of the prey. Sometimes, of course, other predators or scavengers may feed from a carcass, forcing its killer to kill again.

Young birds of prey eat nothing on the day that they hatch, probably because their necks are unsteady and, as they have to reach up and take the morsel offered by the mother bird (they do not gape as most young birds do), they are probably unable to feed then. By the second day, though, the neck muscles are stronger, and they are able to take food offered to them. The appetite usually increases more quickly in the smaller birds than in some of the larger species which take longer to reach maturity.

A young Black-shouldered Kite at sixteen days often weighs more than its parents. It is by no means fully developed, however, merely very fat. At the other extreme, the young of large vultures may not reach their adult weight until after four months. Tropical birds of prey grow more slowly than do their temperate-zone relatives because their parents have a shorter number of daylight hours to do their hunting. A half grown bird may eat more than twice the amount of food required by its parents. It does little but eat and sleep at this time.

Birds that spend most of their flying-time soaring or still-hunting eat less than do birds that use energy beating their wings rapidly in the chase.

Species living in cold countries are usually larger and have many more downy feathers than do related species from warm countries. Their appetites generally increase by about a tenth in very cold weather, because of the increased need to provide body heat.

Golden Eagle—newly hatched, half grown and nearly fledged

Pellets

As we have already seen, owls prefer to swallow their prey whole. Many other birds of prey will also do so if the prey is small enough. Even with large prey, from which most of the fur or feathers have been plucked, a considerable amount of indigestible material accumulates in the bird's gizzard where it forms a firm pellet. The pellet is bound together with the swallowed fur or feathers to form a cylindrical capsule that can be passed back up the bird's digestive tract. This regurgitation is accomplished with the aid of a pumping movement of the head.

Pellets are normally ejected by a bird eight to twenty-four hours after a meal, but sometimes as much as five days may elapse. Insects and other invertebrate remains are also regurgitated in pellets. Some small hawks and owls have pellets consisting mainly of insect materials.

It is not uncommon to find that a pellet recently disgorged appears shiny. This is caused by a mucous secretion that must play the role of a lubricant in helping the bird to eject the pellet.

Owls are unable to digest bones. If one of their pellets is examined, the whole skeleton of the prey may be found inside. This makes it easy for scientists to discover what owls eat.

Most other birds of prey can digest small bones, and some break down surprisingly large ones. If a small animal or bird has been eaten, there may be no trace of bones at all in the

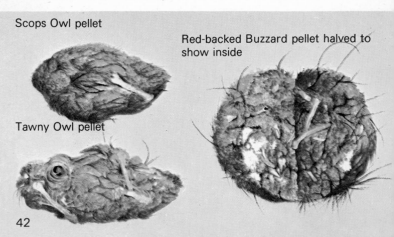

Scops Owl pellet

Red-backed Buzzard pellet halved to show inside

Tawny Owl pellet

42

pellet. When large bones have been eaten and softened, partly digested bone may be ejected—not always in the form of a pellet, as certain birds of prey throw up softened bones in tiny fragments. Pellets also assist in keeping the bird's digestive tract healthy. The soft fur or feathers on the outside of the pellet act like a swab, cleaning the walls of the tract as the pellet is regurgitated.

Pellet formation seems important to the health of most birds, especially while they are young. As birds grow older, however, pellets sometimes become unnecessary. Thus, older birds may avoid eating indigestible parts of their prey. Occasionally fur or feathers may even be harmful.

The best place to find pellets is in the vicinity of the nesting or roosting area. Indeed, the presence of pellets is often the first clue that a particular bird is nesting, or roosting nearby. There are variations between the pellets of an individual bird, depending on the food eaten on the previous day or night. In general, though, birds often regurgitate pellets that are sufficiently characteristic to enable them to be identified.

Examination of the contents of pellets on any given day reveals what the bird in question has recently eaten, but to gain a proper idea of the bird's diet, a careful examination of pellets throughout the year is necessary.

Owls and hawklike birds are not the only birds to eject pellets. Herons, kingfishers, curlews and a variety of other birds that cannot fully digest all of their diet (which may often consist of whole fish) expel the indigestible parts.

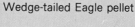

Wedge-tailed Eagle pellet

SEXUAL DIMORPHISM

Among some hawklike birds, the male and female birds are of approximately the same size. But among most raptors, the females are larger than the males. Some hens weigh almost twice as much as their mates. This difference, known as sexual dimorphism, may seem rather strange, but there are very good reasons why it should exist.

In some species, such as those that feed on carrion or snakes, the food taken by both sexes is identical. The methods of locating the food, and of hunting and killing it are also the same for both sexes. In the case of species that hunt birds or mammals, however, the two sexes often take different types of prey.

Brown Harrier Eagles

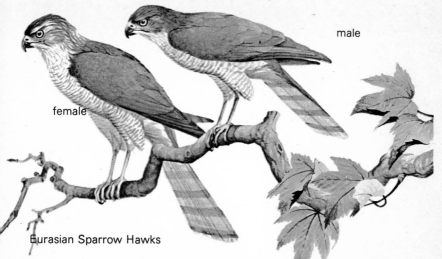

female

male

Eurasian Sparrow Hawks

The majority of diurnal hunters and owls have territories that are rather ill-defined. Nevertheless, in practice the hunting range of the pair is limited. This, in turn, will limit the number of birds or animals available as prey, with interesting implications for the breeding pair. The Northern Sparrow Hawk is a good example. The male is a tiny bird compared to its mate, but is extremely active and very fast and maneuverable over short distances. He specializes in catching small birds up to the size of a thrush. The female, on the other hand, is appreciably larger, much heavier and stronger. She tends to be less active and a little slower, but is more of a specialist in catching medium-sized birds—from thrushes to partridges or even a pigeon if it happens to be slow or weak. As a result, a pair of birds of dissimilar size—because they are adapted to kill different types of quarry—are able to live off a territory that would not support two identical birds.

When food grows scarce in winter or in times of prolonged drought, the female may kill larger prey than she normally would. She may share it with the male. On the other hand, the male may be able to catch something fast-moving, perhaps right at the limit of his capabilities, which he will share with the female.

Although we have here a reason why one sex should be larger than the other, this does not explain why the larger bird should be the female. There are, in fact, excellent reasons why

Peregrine Falcons—female (*front*) snatching pigeon from male

the female should be bigger. All birds of prey tend naturally to keep their catches to themselves.

As young birds in the nest, they have learned to keep their food away from their nest-mates. And as adults, they learn to defend their kills from other predators that may attempt to rob them. When bringing prey to the nest, male birds are thus sometimes rather reluctant to release the food, especially if they are hungry themselves. The female, being the larger, is generally dominant over the male and is able to take prey from him if necessary, and give it to her young.

When the young are first hatched, they are brooded for most of the time by the female, who remains on guard at the nest. The value of having the larger and more aggressive parent left to guard the young while they are small is obvious. During this time, the young require only a moderate amount of food; but it must be of very good quality, generally heart, liver and muscle from prey at the smaller end of the dietary spectrum. For example, several small birds such as tits and finches are better food for young Sparrow Hawks than perhaps a pigeon, although the latter would certainly contain as much nourishment.

Because the male Sparrow Hawk is more agile and active than his mate, he can catch more small prey in the course of a day than she can. Once the young develop beyond a certain point, though, the female ceases to brood them (except at night or in bad weather) and begins hunting herself. At this stage the young need appreciably more food than do the adults, and the female's capacity to catch larger prey becomes very important. The young must then eat almost every part of the carcasses provided to enable them to keep up a maximum rate of growth.

Many of these birds are by nature aggressive and solitary. Therefore, the cooperation required to rear a brood may well be extremely difficult. The reversal in sizes is possibly an adaptation to ensure survival of the species, the male at the nest being dominated by the female who has the important task of looking after the young in the early stages.

Goshawks—male bringing thrush to nest

Bataleur female and nest (*opposite*)

NESTING AND TRAINING THE YOUNG

Pre-nesting and Incubation

Nearly all the Falconiformes and owls take an active interest in their nesting sites well before the time when the female actually lays her eggs. In the case of some of the larger birds of prey, this interest may start several months before laying commences. They may start spending time near the nest and, if it is a large structure, add branches and begin to re-arrange it. Many birds of prey have alternative nest sites, generally two or three and occasionally more. This arrangement is probably an adaptation that aids sanitation, and prevents continued infestation by nest parasites, lice and flies. Many raptors use the same nest year after year, whereas some choose a new site every breeding season. In some species or individuals that return to use the same site and the same nest for some years in succession, the nest itself becomes a huge structure as the material is augmented each spring with extra branches and twigs.

Probably the majority of hawklike birds and owls pair for life. But should one of the pair die, then the other will usually get a new mate fairly quickly, unless it belongs to a species that is rare in the area. Normally pairs that disperse or migrate will return each year to the same nest site at breeding time, and so generally will meet and pair with the mate of the previous year.

During courtship, most Falconiformes species put on aerial displays for the benefit of their mates. For most owls, of course, darkness makes this behavior pointless. So the pair sits together, occasionally rubbing beaks and calling out. Many birds of prey preen each other during courtship, although this seldom happens among the more aggressive species. Most of the larger birds bring a green leafy branch to their mate at the nest, and this 'present' seems somehow to excite both birds.

When the female is about to lay eggs, she stops feeding and begins brooding. After the egg or eggs are laid she spends most of her time incubating. Sometimes the male sits on the eggs; individual pairs vary in this respect. The male normally provides the female with food; she needs less than usual at this time. She will have to incubate for a period between 14 and 52 days, depending on the species.

Golden Eagle's nest in pine tree

Nests

Birds of prey may build their nests almost anywhere. Ideally the nest should be inaccessible to other predators and sheltered from wind, rain, and hot sunshine.

Among the best sites for nests are on sheltered rock ledges and holes in trees, in buildings or in the ground. A small cave on a mountainside is equally advantageous. Moreover, nests built at such sites generally require less material and are easier to construct than those situated in treetops.

Many of the birds that nest in trees prefer to use the vacated nests of other species. But others, including all the eagles, build their own nests, which may be enormous structures. They are added to year after year, until they become so heavy they fall. Sometimes the tree is unable to withstand the weight of the nest, and the supporting branches shatter.

One Golden Eagle's eyrie in a pine tree was seventeen feet deep and five feet across. Nests about ten feet deep may contain more than a ton of sticks. Occasionally, the whole tree topples under the weight of such tremendous structures — particularly in high winds.

A Crowned Hawk Eagle's nest in South Africa has been in use for more than 70 years. As long as it is not on the top-most branches, a tree nest has the advantage of giving shade to the sitting bird and its young. Tree nests, though, are generally less sheltered and safe than crag nests.

Birds that live in drylands often build nests in large cactus-like plants with sharp spines and poisonous sap. Such sites minimize danger from the ground, but nests on top are exposed to the sun and vulnerable to attack from the air.

A large number of raptorial birds nest on the ground in steppe or desert country; and in marshland, there is often no alternative site. The nest may be placed on a rise or in a small pile of stones, a reed bed or other cover. On islands where there are few other predators, birds of prey often nest on the exposed shore.

Osprey's nest on island shore and (*below*) Cape Vulture's nest on cliff ledge

Eggs

Hawklike birds and owls lay fewer eggs than do most other orders of birds. Many of the larger species lay only one or two eggs, and not all breed every year. Most of the smaller species lay between three and five eggs annually.

In the Arctic, birds of prey lay up to nine eggs when prey is plentiful, as in years when lemmings swarm. But when prey is scarce they may lay one or two eggs or none at all. Raptorial birds lay eggs of a size in proportion to the hen's size. Natural selection does not favor the birds producing a large egg, because a female making a kill while carrying an egg inside her might easily break it, which would probably prove fatal to her. Females in captivity lose their appetites a day or two before they lay, probably for this reason. On the other hand, no bird of prey can lay a very tiny egg, because the young must be sufficiently developed when hatched to be able to eat and digest raw meat.

The eggs of birds of prey are rounded at one end and pointed at the other. This shape assures that the egg will not roll out of a stick nest or off a rocky ledge. Many eggs are beautifully marked with reddish-brown hues, sometimes almost orange, and various other shades of brown, sometimes nearly purple. Others are white or off-white. Many of these—like those of most eagles—are pale green when first laid but turn white after two or three days. There is considerable variation in the markings of eggs in some species.

Owls' eggs are quite different. Although they sometimes occupy the nests of other birds, most owls nest in holes. As a result their eggs are unlikely to roll out of the nest. The eggs remain almost completely round since the evolution of a more complicated shape was never necessary. Nesting in holes as they do, they require no camouflage to hide them from predators, so they are invariably white.

As might be expected, the largest eggs are those of the Andean and California Condor, measuring $4\frac{1}{4}$ inches by $2\frac{2}{3}$ inches. The eggs of the larger eagles measure about 3 inches by $2\frac{1}{8}$ inches and weigh five to six ounces. Some other sizes, in inches, are: Buzzard, $2\frac{1}{4}$x$1\frac{3}{4}$; Kestrel, $1\frac{3}{8}$x$1\frac{1}{4}$; Red-thighed Falconet, $1\frac{1}{8}$x$\frac{7}{8}$; Great Eagle Owl, $2\frac{1}{3}$x2; Barn Owl, $1\frac{3}{8}$x$1\frac{1}{4}$; and Pygmy Owl, $1\frac{1}{8}$x1.

White-tailed
Sea Eagle

Egyptian Vulture

Tawny Owl

Great Eagle Owl

Kestrel

53

Bat Falcon dropping Black-
throated Green Warbler
to young

Care and Training of Young

Good parents are as important to young birds of prey as they are to any other creatures, including human beings. We have already seen that the young are cared for continually by the mother, while the father provides all the food, until the family needs so much food that the female must herself begin hunting again. As the young get larger, they begin to learn to dismember carcasses for themselves. Prey is merely brought into the nest and left there by the adults. This is the first real work the young learn to do; it is the first step toward independence.

Young birds of prey are not normally starved into leaving the nest. They often practice flapping their wings at the edge of the nest, and sometimes leave accidently in a gust of wind. At other times the sight of a parent or brother or sister feeding on a nearby branch will provide the incentive. Usually they suddenly seem to make up their minds to go and they are off.

The early flights are uncertain and landings are awkward, but flying ability steadily improves with continual practice. Among species that live entirely off airborne prey, a very high flying standard must be reached in youth and the parents continue to coach the birds for some time. Species that feed off carrion or slow-moving prey achieve independence earlier.

Often adult birds play aerial games with their young, chasing after offspring—diving, twisting, looping, making sharp turns and other maneuvers. Sometimes the parent carries prey and encourages the young to try to take it away. The parent eventually releases the prey, but not before the young bird has had a struggle. Parent birds often attempt to improve the young's skill by passing food to it in mid-air, or by dropping food for it to catch in flight. Young birds will attempt to catch any falling objects, such as leaves, feathers and flying insects, thus increasing their skill.

Gradually their ability improves. Full independence may come in a few weeks—or, as is the case among the eagles, at the end of the first year.

KEEPING BIRDS OF PREY

Falconry

The art of falconry has been carried on in Asia for more than 4,000 years, flourishing there in various forms until modern times. Today, falconry is widely practiced in Arabia, Turkestan, India and Pakistan, and to a more limited extent in Japan. In central Asia, Golden Eagles are trained by man to kill wolves and foxes and the Bonelli's Eagle is used to catch gazelles. Arabs use the Saker to hunt gazelles. This falcon is not strong enough to kill the quarry, but slows down the gazelle by hanging on until it can be reached by hounds schooled to work with the birds. Arabs also use Peregrines and Lanners to catch other birds.

In India the Laggar replaces the Lanner. Although the

Golden Eagle flying at wolf

Lagger is used against crows and partridges, larger and stronger Peregrines and Sakers are preferred for such prey. The little Red-headed Merlin is sometimes used against smaller birds. The Goshawk is very popular in India, and Sparrow Hawks and Shikras are flown at small birds.

Falconry had spread into Europe by A.D. 500, and by the Middle Ages had become the sport of nobility. After A.D. 1000 most European kings spent vast sums on falconry establishments. First-class birds were sold for up to £ 1,000, today equivalent to several thousands of dollars.

In northern Europe today, falconry is still practised quite extensively. The birds are similar to those used in Asia, although recently several species from other parts of the world have come into favor. Since early this century, falconry has gained a hold in the United States where some new species

Peregrine stooping at grouse

Goshawk on bow perch.

including the Cooper's Hawk have proved themselves to be quite adaptable to this interesting sport.

Only those with a deep ambition and qualities of patience and dedication should attempt to master the art of falconry. Ideally, the novice should learn from an expert — an expert being someone whom other falconers respect, whose birds live for a long time, appear in good condition and have a proven record of catching quarry. Much can be learned from books on falconry, but such information is generally not enough by itself to turn the novice into a falconer.

A falconer must choose a bird suitable for hunting the type of land he has at his disposal for the quarry available there. Normally, short-winged hawks are used in wooded country, because this is where they hunt naturally. They do not fly far, so they do not get lost easily—as would a falcon which should be chosen only for open country.

Young hawks are more easily trained than are adults. On the other hand, the full-grown birds are usually much better natural hunters. When a falconer receives a bird, he normally places a hood over its head to keep it quiet. He attaches a leather strap, known as a *jess,* to each leg. The jesses are then fastened to a steel swivel. A leash should be attached to the other end of the swivel, and then secured to the perch. Thus, the bird is tied to its perch in such a way that it has considerable freedom of movement. Falcons often seem to prefer to roost on a wooden or stone block.

The perch or block should be kept in a darkened quiet room or shed. Thus, the hawk will get the impression that it is night and will relax.

A falconer carries the hooded bird on a gloved arm and fist around the dark room for long periods to get it used to being handled, touching it often with a small stick—which

Gyr Falcon on block.

59

Various equipment

it resents but eventually becomes used to. A morsel of food can thus be used instead of the stick, which the bird may at first snap at in anger. If at first small pieces of food are flicked away in annoyance, eventually hunger will overcome this and the bird accepts the food. Soon the hawk comes to expect small morsels, devouring them readily. Larger pieces can then be given. Finding these too large to swallow, it will transfer them to its feet and begin to feed normally. The handler must always keep in mind that these are potentially dangerous birds and that this is not a sport for children.

After this stage the light in the room may be increased gradually. Or, if the hawk is still hooded, the hood may be removed for a few moments just as the hungry bird is beginning to eat a particularly succulent piece of meat. If this is arranged and carried out carefully, the hawk may continue feeding without becoming upset. At first the falconer should turn his face away, never appearing to stare directly at the bird or it will take fright.

Once the hawk remains steady on the falconer's glove in full light, the next step is to take the bird outside. Late on a quiet, still evening is usually the best time for this first excursion. Afterward, the bird should gradually be allowed to grow accustomed to being carried about at other times

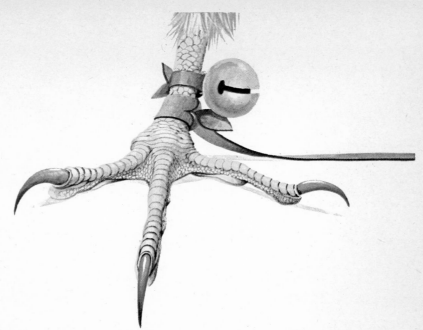

of the day. It should be introduced to other people, animals, vehicles, and so on—at first at a distance, then gradually at closer ranges. At this stage the hawk can be encouraged to jump from its perch to the fist for its food, if possible over a longer distance each day. It should then be taken outside to a familiar place and encouraged to fly long distances to food while attached to a line called a *creance*.

When the falconer is finally certain that his bird will fly to his fist automatically, he releases it from the creance at feeding time. Having made certain that there will be no disturbance in the area, he may safely fly the bird for the first time. Before this, while still attached to a line, a hawk may be trained to take its food from a *lure,* a dummy usually made from leather and the wings of the hawk's intended quarry.

First, the lure (with a large piece of good meat tied to it) is tossed a foot or two in front of the sitting bird, which will jump onto it if hungry. After the hawk becomes accustomed to such feeding, the falconer drags the lure along the ground and the bird flies after it. Eventually the bird will snatch at it as it is swung in the air. Falcons are often exercised this way for long periods, the falconer jerking the lure away at the last moment so that the bird is forced to circle up and dive again. Falcons do not become annoyed; they seem to regard this as a game, knowing that they will be allowed to catch the lure eventually.

The lure is the best way to encourage a bird to return if it seems disinclined to do so. A whistle is often used as the lure is swung to attract the bird's attention, and the sight of the food moving below lures it down. A bell attached to the bird will help the falconer locate his hunter if it is lost or temporarily out of sight. The falconer generally attaches a small bell to the hawk's leg just above the jess by means of a piece of leather known as a *bewit.*

Sometimes a bird of prey will decide to chase something else while waiting for the lure and hence make its first true kill. Captive birds or animals are often released close to the hawk to encourage it to make its first kill. This method is, however, illegal in most countries today. Generally a falconer will attempt to get his bird close to its quarry, trying to choose one that is immature, in molt, or well away from cover to give his inexperienced bird a good chance. But some hawks become very tame and simply wait for food to be produced, never becoming good hunters. Such birds, of no use to a falconer, may make good pets.

Box cage diagram

Height slightly greater than depth.

approx. 2 ft.

3 – 4 ft

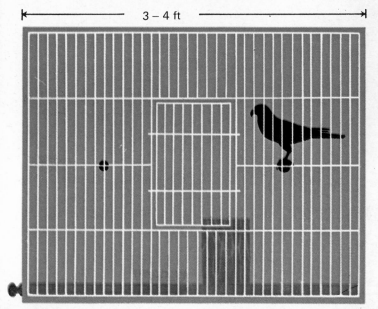

Shed for larger birds

Which species to choose for a pet depends partly on the accommodation available. A large box cage of about three to four feet in length, nearly two feet in width, and slightly more in height is suitable for most of the smaller owls and falcons. A cage of this size may also be used for small hawks. Hawks are less suitable as indoor pets because their droppings are ejected with some force for several hours after they have fed, and the cage and its surroundings are difficult to keep clean.

The floor of the cage should be covered with a metal tray that slides out for cleaning. It may be scrubbed off every day or covered with peat; on no account should sand be used. Two perches should be provided, one at each side of the cage and far enough in for the bird's tail to miss the sides if it leans forward. The perches should be thick, about the span of the bird's toes in diameter. A small wooden block and a dish of water should also be provided. Wire mesh should not be used for the front of the cage; a wire frame with as few horizontal bars as possible, or thin wooden slats will do less damage to the bird's feathers. The door—about nine inches high and seven inches wide—should be at the center. A tame bird should be allowed to leave or enter the cage freely, provided that it has not just been fed, that highly polished surfaces and mirrors have been covered to protect them from claws, breakable ornaments have been put away and the windows closed.

A garden shed makes suitable accommodation for most large birds. Seven feet by five feet is a good size, but a large owl or a medium-sized eagle requires more space. The furniture should be the same as that in the box cage and the floor should consist of peat or clean soil. There should be one large wire window facing approximately south, with small ventilators at the ends of the shed which may be opened in hot weather. Small trees should be close by to give shade.

In general, more than one bird should not be confined in the same cage. If someone wants to keep two or more in a large shed, a device known as a screen perch should be run the length of the room. Each bird is tied to the screen perch by a leash attached to its jesses, at about four or five foot intervals. With some species, pairs may be kept loose in a shed together and sometimes a small group of mixed species (usually insectivorous or carrion-eating kinds) may get along together. Kites, buzzards and vultures, and some of the smaller eagles are species that will usually live well together. Hawks, falcons, kestrels, and most large eagles are best kept alone, otherwise they are likely to fight and may even kill one another.

Owls usually do well in pairs, but except in the case of scops owls it is unwise to try trios. The training of owls differs in that they should be handled in bright artificial light, which makes them drowsy. Once tame, they are more inclined to fly for food in dull evening light. They are also more likely to breed in captivity than are birds of prey. But a large quantity of natural food (mice, small birds) is required for both the adults prior to breeding and for the young.

Raw, lean beef usually forms the basic diet for raptorial birds in captivity. The approximate amounts required by birds of different sizes is given on page 39. Meat should be cut into small strips for the smaller insectivorous species and into long strips for snake eaters. Most of the large, strong-footed species ought to be given beef bones on which to exercise their beaks and neck muscles. Many species naturally eat fish; meal worms and blow-fly larvae are fine for small hawks and owls. Entire animals, such as mice for small species, and rabbits for larger ones, are necessary at regular intervals to provide essential roughage, vitamins and minerals. This balanced diet is essential. Amounts of food given must be controlled carefully; too much is almost as harmful as too little, although an occasional gorge will do no harm. Birds should always show enthusiasm at their feeding time.

Most birds of prey enjoy being placed outside on their blocks or perches for a while each day. They appreciate both the rain and the sunshine. Strong winds unsettle them, and they must not be left out in really bad weather.

Pet Tawny Owl

SYSTEMATIC LIST OF HAWKLIKE BIRDS AND OWLS

American Vultures

The seven surviving species of the family Cathartidae, the American, or Cathartid, Vultures, are the descendants of a once much more widespread group of birds. They were probably once found throughout the world, and fossil remains have been found in Europe. Numerous fossils have also been found in California, including some species far larger than any vultures living today. One of these, *Teratornis incredibilis*, had a wing span of 17 feet. Others, including *Teratornis merriami*, that only became extinct comparatively recently, possessed wing spreads of 12 to 14 feet.

Birds of this size could survive only in ideal surroundings, for they required a large amount of food as well as good weather conditions in which to glide and soar. Taking off must have been very difficult when the birds had a full crop.

Despite these shortcomings, two very large members of the family have survived. They are the California Condor *(Gymnogyps californianus)*, and the Great or Andean Condor *(Vultur gryphus)*, both 40 to 46 inches in length. Both birds are similar in wing spread, spanning 9 to 10 feet and weighing from 20 to 28 pounds. The Andean Condor is found throughout almost all the Andes Mountains, from sea level to above 15,000 feet. Although declining in some areas, it still holds its own in many places. It feeds mostly on carrion—dead llamas, cattle, sheep, and so on. Where it comes down to the shore in remote areas it will feed on stranded marine mammals, including whales. It is an extremely strong

King Vulture; Mexico and South America.

Andean Condor;
South America

Red-headed Turkey Vulture; North and South America

Greater Yellow-headed Turkey Vulture; South Amer

bird, and has been known to kill sick llamas and even horses if it is really hungry. Young birds are brown; adults are black and silver-gray. This is the only species of American vulture which may be easily sexed—as the male has a yellow eye and a wattle above the beak. The female lacks the wattle and has a red eye.

Probably the nearest relative of the Andean Condor is the King Vulture (*Sarcorhamphus papa*). Measuring 30 to 32 inches long, it is a smaller bird with a wing spread of 6 feet or more. An inhabitant of tropical forests from Mexico to northern Argentina, it does not ascend the mountains as it cannot withstand frost. A strong bird, it can drive other vultures from carrion and apparently is able to kill snakes. Young birds are brown and adults at six years are black and pinkish-white, with an orange wattle on a dark head.

The American Black Vulture (*Coragyps atratus*) is a small vulture, 22 to 26 inches long, with a wing spread of a little more than 4 feet and weighing 4½ pounds. These birds are gregarious and congregate where food is likely to be abundant. Being short-winged, it spends less time in the air than do other species and so are not able to search a very large area. Although normally a carrion eater feeding on dead animals, fish washed up on the shore, and garbage, this bird will occasionally eat birds' eggs and has been known to kill young pigs.

Black Vulture with Cottontail; southern U.S., Mexico and South America.

There are three species of turkey vultures. Two are tropical South American birds—the Yellow-headed (*Cathartes burrovianus*) and the Greater Yellow-headed (*C. melambrotus*) species. The former has a maximum body length of about 26 inches, while the latter species grows half a foot bigger. The third bird, the Red-headed Turkey Vulture, falls between the previous two in size and ranges all over the Americas from Canada to Tierra del Fuego and the Falkland Islands.

The Red-headed and Greater Yellow-headed species are long-winged, with spans of six feet. They fly and glide low to the ground, like harriers, in search of carrion. The turkey vultures are unique among their relatives in that they can locate a decaying carcass through their sense of smell, and like many other vultures, they are splendid soarers.

The California Condor, of which only some 40 birds are still in existence, is actually a gigantic turkey vulture. Like the Andean Condor, it breeds high on mountains and lays only one egg per clutch. Condors do not breed every year, further contributing to the smallness of the living population. The rest of the American vultures breed nearer sea level, on the ground among bushes, among rocks, in hollow trees, and even in old ruins. These smaller vultures lay two eggs and as a rule breed annually.

Secretary Bird and Osprey

The Secretary Bird (*Sagittarius serpentarius*) lives in savannah country south of the Sahara in Africa. In a real sense, it is a 'pedestrian' bird of prey, since its chief means of locomotion are its long, stiltlike legs—an adaption like that of the African grasslands' flightless ostrich. Poised on its long legs, the Secretary scrutinizes the grass for a variety of snakes, lizards, small rodents, young birds and large insects. Because the bird's feet must serve as a means of locomotion, they are necessarily less specialized for killing than are those of other raptors. Hence, it has evolved a curious *coup de grâce*—a hard stamp of the foot. Usually, the Secretary recoils a yard or so after each hit, circles the quarry, then jumps in again, giving another blow with the foot. The method is particularly safe and effective against snakes, which make up much of its diet. Although the Secretary employs its claws in the kill, it does so to a lesser degree than other predacious birds. Secretary Birds fly less frequently than other raptors. They lay two eggs per clutch, generally on a low, flat-topped bush.

Secretary Bird with python;
southern Africa.

The Osprey (*Pandion haliaetus*), 23 to 24 inches in length, is highly specialized at catching fish. Its well-adapted foot, with two toes facing in each direction, and sharply pointed scales below each claw enable it to grip the slippery, wriggling fish. It will sometimes still-hunt from a perch beside a lake, but usually it flies fairly low and immediately hovers upon sighting a movement in the water below. Should the movement be made by a fish of the right size swimming near the surface, the Osprey dives. It enters the water feet first and can submerge if necessary to clutch its quarry. It is the only bird of prey able to do so, its plumage being extremely waterproof. Large fish have been caught with the skeleton of an Osprey attached to their backs, showing that the birds occasionally strike quarry which is too strong for them. Ospreys are found almost throughout the world, except in the polar regions. Normally they breed on islands, sometimes in very dense colonies. Their two or three eggs are laid in a large nest made of branches, seaweed, driftwood or dead vegetable matter on a tree, old building, or on the ground.

Osprey; world-wide.

Black Baza;
India to Malaya.

Kites

Among the most primitive of the Falconiformes are the many kinds of kites, long-winged, mostly long-tailed birds, experts at soaring and circling.

Cuckoo falcons or bazas are small birds, 15 to 17 inches long, that inhabit forests in Africa, Madagascar, southeast Asia, and northern Australasia. They hunt most often at dawn and dusk, sometimes in small parties, searching the trees for small prey, including bats. Their most unusual feature is the possession of two serrations in the upper mandible, an adaptation that assists them in holding and dismembering large insects, and probably helps when killing even larger prey, since their feet are rather weak.

There are five species and all have crests. The African Cuckoo Falcon (*Aviceda cuculoides*) has a brown back with a grayish head and chest, and a white belly banded with rufous. The Madagascar Cuckoo Falcon (*Aviceda madagascariensis*) has three black stripes on the throat and is white-breasted with rufous streaks. Jerdon's Baza (*Aviceda jerdoni*), found from Sikkim to Sumatra, has a black crest tipped with white.

The Crested Baza (*Aviceda subcristata*) of Australia and nearby islands has a shorter crest, with rufous thighs and underwings. The Black Baza (*Aviceda leuphotes*) inhabits much of India, Burma and Malaya and is much smaller than the others, 11 inches.

Two small species of the South American jungles, the Double-toothed Kite (*Harpagus bidentatus*) and the Rufous-thighed Kite (*H. diodon*), both 12 to 14 inches, are similar in habits to the cuckoo falcons. They too have double-toothed beaks. The sexes are quite different in the Double-toothed Kite; males are dark brown on the back, grayer on the head, with barred-gray and white breasts. Females are brown below with white barring on the belly. The Rufous-thighed Kite, apart from its thighs, is light gray below.

The Bat-eating Buzzard (*Machaerhamphus alcinus*), 16 to 19 inches, of southern Africa, Indonesia and New Guinea, is the most nocturnal of all the hawklike birds. It resembles a large, dark cuckoo falcon and has very long wings, giving it the great speed required to catch its quarry. As well as killing

Bat-eating Buzzard diving at bat; southern Africa and southeast Asia.

75

bats, it takes insects and small birds. It builds a nest in a tree, generally producing two eggs. Cuckoo falcons lay from one to three eggs and Double-toothed Kites from three to four.

Another kite with a pronounced tooth on its upper mandible is the Cayenne or Gray-headed Kite (*Leptodon cayanensis*), 17 to 20 inches, which lives in lowland forests from southern Mexico to northern Argentina. It has large wings and a long, black and gray barred tail. It is black above, white below, and has a light gray head. It is reputed to catch small birds but is probably almost exclusively insectivorous.

The Hook-billed Kite (*Chondrohierax uncinatus*), 14 to 15 inches, inhabits the same range as the gray-headed species. Males are dark slate above, and gray, narrowly barred with white or sandy, or completely gray below. Females have slate-colored heads and a reddish half collar. Their breasts are sandy, barred brown. Sometimes both sexes are bluish-slate all over. This bird feeds on tree snails, insects, reptiles and birds.

The Snail, or Everglade, Kite (*Rostrhamus sociabilis*), 15½ to 16½ inches, ranges over a similar area to the two previous kites, in addition to Florida and Cuba. It feeds entirely on fresh-water snails, its long hooked bill being specially adapted to extract these from their shells. The male is shown on the opposite page; females are deep brown, the underparts lightly streaked and have a white streak over each eye and a white rump.

The Slender-billed Kite (*R. hamatus*) of northern South America is slightly smaller, with an even longer bill and

Honey Buzzard;
Europe and Asia.

stronger legs and feet. It has dark plumage throughout. Its habits are the same as those of the Snail Kite. Both birds nest in scattered colonies, usually in rushes. Two to four eggs are laid.

The Honey Buzzard (*Pernis apivorus*), 20 to 24 inches, is a kite that superficially resembles a buzzard. These birds summer throughout Europe and Asia from Britain to Borneo. In winter, they move to Africa and southern Asia, where they may sometimes be identified by their possession of a crest. The plumage of this species, however, is very variable throughout its range. The Barred Honey Buzzard (*P. celebensis*), 20 to 22 inches, of Celebes and the Philippines is heavily barred with brown and white on the breast. These birds raid the nests of wasps and bees for grubs and honeycomb, but will also take mammals and birds. They usually use old nests of other birds, but sometimes they build their own. Two eggs are normally laid.

The Long-tailed Honey Buzzard (*Henicopernis longicauda*), 20 to 22 inches, of New Guinea and surrounding islands, has a dark brown back barred with gray, and is whitish with dark streaks below. The New Britain strain is smaller (18 inches long) and darker. Some authorities recognize it as a distinct species, known as the Black or Gurney's Honey Buzzard (*H. infuscata*).

The Plumbeous Kite (*Ictinia plumbea*), 15 inches, inhabits open country dotted with groups of tall trees from Mexico to northern Argentina. It is dark gray above and pale gray below

Snail, or Everglade, Kite; southern U.S., Mexico and South America.

77

with two white bars on the tail. The Mississippi Kite (*I. misisippiensis*), 14 inches, found in the southeastern United States in summer, migrating further south in winter, is similar but its tail is entirely black. In flight, these kites look like falcons, searching for insects high in the air. They generally nest in high trees, laying one to three eggs annually.

The Swallow-tailed Kite (*Elanoides forficatus*), 24 inches, is found on low ground near water, from the southern United States to northern Argentina. This beautiful bird is often seen in small flocks soaring high in the air, where it captures large insects. It will also take tree frogs, lizards and snakes from the upper branches of trees. It nests high in tall trees, laying two or three eggs.

The African Swallow-tailed Kite (*Chelictinia riocourii*), 15 inches, is found in open country from Senegal to the Sudan and Kenya. It looks very graceful and slender in flight. Its plumage is light gray above and white below. It lives mainly on insects and is usually seen in small flocks hawking them

Swallow-tailed Kite; southern U.S., Mexico and South America.

high in the air. However, it also hunts for insects on the ground, as well as lizards and mice. It makes a nest in a small thorn'tree where it lays three or four eggs.

The Pearl Kite (*Gampsonyx swainsonii*), 8 inches, lives in lightly wooded savannah and the edges of forest in northern and central South America. Its plumage is mixed dark brown and gray above, rufous on the neck and side, and white with black patches below. Its food consists of insects, lizards and occasionally mice and small birds. It breeds in tall trees in small colonies, each nest containing three eggs.

The Black-shouldered Kite (*Elanus caeruleus*), 11 to 14 inches, is found in Portugal, Africa and southeastern Asia. The White-tailed Kite (*E. leucurus*), 16 inches, of the New World and the Australian Black-shouldered Kite (*E. notatus*), 13 to 14 inches, are very similar. The two last mentioned show a black mark under the wing joint. The Letter-winged Kite (*E. scriptus*) of south and central Australia is similar to the Black-shouldered species but has a black bar running along the forward edge of the wing. Rats and other rodents are its main food, supplemented with small reptiles, frogs and birds. It generally flies slowly when hunting, hovering frequently. It also still-hunts from trees, wires and poles. The four kites in this group all build small nests in trees, generally laying three to four eggs.

The size of the Black Kite (*Milvus migrans*) varies between

Black-shouldered Kite hovering; Portugal, Africa and southeast Asia.

Black Kite; Old World

18 and 25 inches, depending on the geographic region in which the birds dwell. Among the commonest birds of prey, the Black Kite ranges over most of the Old World from Spain to Australia. It is light in weight—between 1 and 1½ pounds—and its long wings and tail give it a wonderful buoyant flight. It soars for much of the day, descending to pick up small prey or carrion. It usually nests in trees, occasionally on rocks or buildings. Sometimes several pairs nest together. Three eggs form the usual clutch. The Red Kite (*M. milvus*), 22 to 24 inches, is found in Wales, Europe, northeast Africa and the

Red Kite—flight silhouette

Cape Verde Islands. It is a more majestic bird than the Black Kite, with even longer wings and tail; it is reddish-brown in color. It takes bigger prey than the Black Kite. It builds its nest in trees, and usually lays three eggs.

The Square-tailed Kite (*Lophoictinia isura*) of Australia is 20 inches in size. It is similar to the Red Kite, but the tail is shorter and slightly notched. It flies lower than do most kites when hunting—like a harrier—and catches young birds, reptiles, and even caterpillars. It lays two or three eggs in tree nests, which it usually builds near water.

The Black-breasted Kite (*Hamirostra melanosternon*), 21 to 24 inches, is another Australian species, more heavily built and shorter tailed than the square-tailed species. Some birds are similar in coloring to the Square-tailed Kite; others have black heads and breasts. It preys mainly on rabbits and lizards, also eating eggs. It will break an Emu's egg with a stone. It nests in trees where it normally lays two eggs.

The Brahminy Kite (*Haliastur indus*), 17 to 20 inches, is found from India to northern Australia, and the Whistling Kite or Whistling Eagle (*H. sphenurus*), 20 to 22 inches, is found over most of Australia, New Guinea and nearby islands. The Whistling Kite is a brown bird with buffish markings. Both birds will eat almost any sort of animal from locusts and other insects to fish (dead or alive), frogs, reptiles, young birds and small mammals. Some Whistling Kites regularly catch rabbits. Both species live near water, on the coast or inland. They nest in trees, laying two and sometimes three eggs.

Brahminy Kite;
India, southeast Asia
and Australia.

Sea Eagles

The eight species of sea eagles are probably closely related to kites but are far more massive and heavier birds. They have evolved much broader wings to keep them airborne, the wing span varying between 5½ and 7½ feet. Their tails are mostly wedge-shaped. There are four smaller sea eagles. The White-bellied Sea Eagle (*Haliaeetus leucogaster*), 25 to 27 inches, is found on sea coasts from India to Australia; it is gray-backed with white head and underparts. Sanford's Sea Eagle (*H. sanfordi*), 25 to 28 inches, of the Solomon Islands, is dark brown above and rufous brown below. The African Sea Eagle (*H. vocifer*), 23 to 29 inches, ranges along the coast, lakes and rivers in Africa south of the Sahara. The Madagascar Sea Eagle (*H. vociferoides*), 23 to 26 inches, is mainly brown with rufous streaking on the head and underparts; its cheeks and tail are white.

The four larger sea eagles are: Pallas's Sea Eagle (*H. leu-*

Bald Eagle;
North America

coryphus), 27 to 32 inches, found from the Caspian Sea to the Amur River and in India and Burma. It is brown with a buff head and neck, and a broad white band across the rounded tail. The Bald Eagle (*H. leucocephalus*) of North America and the national emblem of the United States, is 30 to 36 inches in length, has a dark brown body with a pure white head. The White-tailed or Gray Sea Eagle (*H. albicilla*), 27 to 38 inches, is found in Greenland, Iceland, much of Europe, and in northern and central Asia. Steller's Sea Eagle (*H. pelagicus*), 35 to 41 inches, originates in northeast Asia. Besides the bird illustrated on the following page, there is an all-black color phase with a white tail.

Steller's Sea Eagle;
northeast Asia

Sea eagles take a wide range of prey. The smaller species feed mainly on fish captured no more than a foot beneath the surface. Sanford's Sea Eagle also takes birds and mammals.

Since larger sea eagles are not very maneuverable, they eat more carrion, and in hunting are generally restricted to sick, injured or immature prey. Sea eagles are among the most vocal birds of prey. They build huge nests on trees, cliff ledges, among rocks or on the ground in remote treeless areas. Normally one or two eggs are laid. The Pallas's Sea Eagle, however, generally lays three.

African Sea Eagle;
Africa, south of the Sahara.

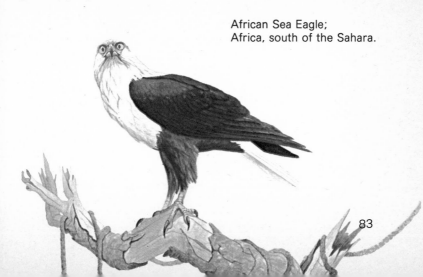

Fishing Eagles

The Gray-headed Fishing Eagle (*Icthyophaga ichthyaetus*), 24 to 29 inches, ranges over most of India, Ceylon and Burma and the Philippines. The Lesser Fishing Eagle (*I. nana*), 20 to 26 inches, inhabits northern India, Burma, the Malay peninsula, Sumatra and Borneo. It is similar in color to the Gray-headed Fishing Eagle but its tail is completely dark brown. The Lesser Fishing Eagles dwell at lakes, rivers and marshes. The Gray-headed species occupies the sea coast. They live almost entirely on fish but have been known to take reptiles, ground birds and small mammals. Their outer claw is reversible like the Osprey's, and they have similar pointed scales on the undersides of the toes—adaptations for grasping slippery, wriggling fish. Unlike the sea eagles, these birds have short wings, 3 feet 9 inches to 5 feet across. It is not surprising,

Gray-headed Fishing Eagle;
India, southeast Asia
and the Philippines

Vulturine Fish Eagle;
Africa south of
the Sahara.

therefore, that fishing eagles spend most of the day in trees, seldom flying far. Like sea eagles, they catch fish within a foot of the surface and are highly vocal. They often call at night. Their nests are in tall trees and they lay up to three eggs.

The Vulturine Fish Eagle or Palm Nut Vulture (*Gypohierax angolensis*), 22 to 25 inches, can be found over much of Africa south of the Sahara. Its distribution depends on the presence of the oil palm and raffia palm, the nuts of which are important items in its diet. It also eats fish (generally dead ones), crabs and small carrion. Its strong foot permits the killing of mammals of about its own weight — that is, 3 to 4 pounds. Like the other fishing eagles, it has a variety of call notes, coughs, mews and growls. It builds its large nests either in tall trees or in the hollowed out centers of the huge nut clusters of the raffia palm. It lays only one egg. During the nesting season these birds perform aerial dives from very high up, in a manner similar to the sea eagles.

Vultures

The White-headed Vulture (*Trigonoceps occipitalis*), 30 to 32 inches, is found over most of Africa south of Sierra Leone and the Sudan. It is less of a true vulture than any of the following species. This bird is solitary except in the breeding season when a pair and an immature bird may hunt together. They look more eagle-like than do other vultures. The tail is square, making it more maneuverable, and it has a fairly strong foot — adaptations enabling it to kill the young of small antelopes and birds such as the young of the Lesser Flamingos. When hungry, they can drive most other vultures away from the carcass.

The Cinereous Vulture (*Aegypius monachus*), 42 to 45

Left:
1 Ruppell's Vulture
2 Immature Ruppell's
3 Lappet-faced Vulture
4 Immature Lappet-faced Vulture
5 White-headed Vulture
6 Egyptian Vulture
7 White-backed Vulture
8 Hooded Vultures

Griffon Vulture (*right*), Spain to northern India.

inches, is a huge dark brown bird. On average it is the largest bird of prey in the Old World, some individuals having a wing span of more than 9 feet. It is found from Spain through southeastern Europe and across central and eastern Asia. It is generally seen singly or in small groups. Although a carrion eater, this species is very powerful, using its strength to drive other birds from a carcass.

The Lappet-faced or Sociable Vulture (*Torgos tracheliotus*), 40 to 45 inches, is another vulture generally seen singly or in family groups. Found over the drier parts of Africa and Palestine, it dominates all other African vultures at the carcass when hungry. Its huge beak enables it to tear off and gulp down large chunks of muscle.

The Pondicherry or Indian Black Vulture (*Sarcogyps calvus*), 30 to 32 inches, is indigenous to India, Burma and the Malay peninsula. It is a black vulture with huge reddish lappets of skin hanging from its face and patches of white on its chest and above the thighs. These birds are usually seen in pairs. Because of its small size, it is not dominant at carcasses, but with its large bill it can tear off sufficient food for itself very rapidly, making the most of its uncertain opportunities. The four solitary vultures described above build large nests high in trees and normally lay only one egg.

Griffons are large vultures that live in colonies in mountainous country. There are five species. The Himalayan Griffon Vulture (*Gyps himalayensis*), 41 to 43 inches — on average, the second largest bird of prey in the Old World — is a huge brownish-white bird with a wing span of about 9 feet; it is native to Asia. The Griffon Vulture (*G. fulvus*), 39 to 41 inches, is a darker bird found from Spain to northern India. The Cape

Bearded Vulture *or* Lammergeyer;
southern Europe, Africa
and Asia.

Griffon Vulture (*G. coprotheres*), 39 to 41 inches, of South Africa is similar but paler. Ruppell's Griffon (*G. ruppellii*), 35 to 37 inches, ranges across Africa from Gambia to Kenya and north to Egypt. It is a brownish-black bird with whitish spots. The Long-billed Vulture (*G. indicus*) of India, Burma and Malaysia, 32 to 34 inches in size, is pale below with a dark or pale brown back. Griffons nest and roost in colonies on cliff ledges, leaving late in the morning to search for food and returning before dusk. They occasionally nest in trees and usually lay only one egg.

Two similar species, the African White-backed Vulture (*G. africanus*) and the Indian White-backed Vulture (*G. bengalensis*), both 30 inches, generally live in large numbers in countries where food is very plentiful. The former are the vultures one normally sees assembling around carcasses in large numbers in films of African game country. Always nesting in trees, they lay a single egg. Large vultures are often quite noisy, particularly when at carcasses, uttering hisses, squeals and roaring sounds.

The Hooded Vulture (*Necrosyrtes monachus*), 24 to 26 inches, is confined to a range concentrated in south-central Africa, below the Congo. It visits carcasses after the larger vultures have eaten and gleans any leftover scraps from the bones. Generally, its feeding habits are crow-like, scavenging almost anywhere for small dead creatures or for garbage. It lays one egg and nests in trees or on cliff ledges.

The Egyptian Vulture (*Neophron percnopterus*), 21 to 26 inches, ranges over southern Europe, most of Africa, and into India. It is similar in habits to the Hooded Vulture. Both birds weigh about 4 pounds, small in contrast to the 10-to-20 pound average of the larger vultures. Egyptian Vultures have a strong foot and are able to kill slow-moving small reptiles and mammals, but they usually scavenge for carrion and refuse. They nest in holes in cliffs and occasionally in trees or buildings, and lay two eggs.

The Lammergeyer (*Gypaetus barbatus*), 37 to 46 inches, is found in remote mountain areas of southern Europe; northern, eastern and southern Africa; and southwestern and central Asia. It feeds on bones and carrion. It flies off with the bones in its feet and drops them onto rocks to shatter them, then alights to eat the marrow and bone fragments. It has been seen to knock an animal off a cliff, then descend to devour the injured creature. It lays two eggs in cave nests in high cliff faces.

Egyptian Vulture; southern Europe, Africa and India.

Harriers

Harriers inhabit open country throughout most of the world, except in polar regions. The Spotted Harrier (*Circus assimilis*), 19 to 24 inches, found from Australia to Celebes, has brown plumage, spotted with white. The Long-winged Harrier (*C. buffoni*), 19 to 23 inches, of South America is black-backed and chested, with a white or black belly. The Black Harrier (*C. maurus*), 19 to 22 inches, of South Africa has blackish-brown plumage with a white rump. The slightly smaller African Marsh Harrier (*C. ranivorus*), 18 to 20 inches, of southern and eastern Africa is nearly as dark; the male has silver-gray on the wings, and both sexes have a barred tail. The Marsh Harrier (*C. aeruginosus*), 19 to 23 inches, is found over most of Europe, North Africa, central Asia, Madagascar, Australia, New Zealand and nearby islands. The European male is illustrated here, but the plumage of both sexes is very variable.

In the next five species the females are brown above with whitish rumps, and pale, darkly streaked bellies. The Pied Harrier (*C. mela-*

90

African Harrier Hawk (*above*). Marsh Harrier; Europe, north Africa, Asia, and Australia (*below*).

Marsh Hawk or Hen
Harrier; North America,
Europe and Asia

noleucus) is 18 to 20 inches long. The male is black on the head, back and wing tips, and whitish elsewhere. The Hen Harrier or Marsh Hawk (*C. cyaneus*), 18 to 22 inches, found over most of Europe, Asia and North America, is gray-backed and gray on the head and chest, and white below. The Cinereous Harrier (*C. cinereus*), 18 to 20 inches, of southwestern South America is similar but banded orange-brown below. The Pallid Harrier (*C. macrourus*), 17 to 20 inches, found from eastern Europe to central Asia is pale gray above and white below. Montagu's Harrier (*C. pygargus*), 16 to 18 inches, found from western Europe to central Asia, is darker gray above with a black bar on the wings. It is streaked brown below. This last species is distinctly smaller than the others.

Harriers hunt mostly by flying low over moors, fields and marshes, surprising water birds, small land birds, rodents, reptiles, and frogs. Most species lay three to six eggs in ground nests. The Spotted Harrier, however, nests in trees.

The Crane Hawk (*Geranospiza caerulescens*), 16 to 20 inches, of Central and South America, is black or gray, the gray ones having white bars on their bellies. The African Harrier Hawk (*Polyboroides typus*), 20 to 27 inches, and the Madagascar Harrier Hawk (*P. radiatus*), 23 to 24 inches, share a curious anatomical trait: they have double-jointed legs—an adaptation for reaching into holes for lizards and other small prey. The Crane Hawk lays one or two eggs in a tree nest; harrier hawks lay two eggs in a tree nest or on the ground in Madagascar.

Eurasian Short-toed Eagle with grass snake

Snake Eagles

The Short-toed Eagle (*Circaetus gallicus*), 26 to 32 inches, is found over southern Europe, most of Africa and southern and central Asia. Southern Saharan strains are more finely barred on the belly than others. Eastern and southern African birds are blackish on the back and chest and white below. The Brown Harrier Eagle (*C. cinereus*), 29 to 31 inches, of Africa south of the Sahara, has a heavier build than the others and is dark brown. The Banded Harrier Eagle (*C. cinerascens*), 25 to 26 inches, is found over much of Africa south of the Sahara, except in the extreme south. It is not unlike the Short-toed Eagle except for a black tail with a broad white band. The Southern Banded Harrier Eagle (*C. fasciolatus*), 23 to 24 inches, of the eastern African coast, is light below, barred brown, and has three black bars on the tail.

The Crested Serpent Eagle (*Spilornis cheela*), 16 to 30 inches, is found from northern India and China—where the largest members of the species occur—to Borneo. The Philippine Serpent Eagle (*S. holospilus*), 23 to 25 inches, is heavily spotted above. The Celebes Serpent Eagle (*S. rufipectus*), 16 to 19 inches, is very dark with a rufous chest; it is banded dark

92

brown below. The Nicobar Serpent Eagle (*S. klossi*), 15 to 16 inches, from Great Nicobar Island is pale-backed and buffish underneath. The Andaman Serpent Eagle (*S. elgini*), 21 inches, is a rufous-brown bird, with a heavily spotted breast.

The Gold Coast Serpent Eagle (*Dryotriorchis spectabilis*), 22 to 23 inches, of west African and Congo forests is a short-winged, long-tailed bird. The Madagascar Serpent Eagle (*Eutriorchis astur*), 23 to 26 inches, has an even longer tail and is white, narrowly banded with black below. The Bateleur (*Terathopius ecaudatus*), 22 to 25 inches, lives in open country in Africa south of the Sahara (see page 48).

All these birds eat snakes and lizards. The Bateleur also eats carrion and kills small mammals, flying up to 200 miles a day in search of food. The Short-toed Eagle hunts open country, hovering while searching the grass for snakes. The other species do a great deal of still-hunting and will take birds and small mammals occasionally. Most species are noisy, uttering loud caws and mewing whistles. Most lay one egg in a small tree-nest.

Crested Serpent Eagle; Asia (*left*).
Gold Coast Serpent Eagle;
west Africa (*right*).

93

Pale Chanting Goshawk;
east and south Africa.

Goshawks and Sparrow Hawks

Doria's Goshawk (*Megatriorchis doriae*), 23 to 27 inches, of New Guinea is brownish-black above, and white with short brown streaks below. It has very short wings and a long tail with twelve bars. The Red Goshawk (*Erythrotriorchis radiatus*), 20 to 23 inches, of northern and eastern Australia, is related to it. Both haunt wooded country, preying on birds, small mammals and snakes. They build large tree nests.

The Long-tailed Hawk (*Urotriorchis macrourus*), 24 inches, found in forests from Ghana to the Congo, catches birds and squirrels in the tree tops, but will also stalk birds on the ground.

The Dark Chanting Goshawk (*Melierax metabates*),

Red Goshawk;
Australia.

Long-tailed Hawk, west Africa.

17 to 20 inches, is found over most of Africa and southern Arabia. The Pale Chanting Goshawk (*M. canorus*), 18 to 21 inches, from eastern and southern Africa, is distinguished from the previous bird by its white rump. Both inhabit dry, open bush country, usually still-hunting from posts, bushes or rocks. They hunt low to the ground like the harriers, feeding mainly on lizards. They nest in bushes or trees, laying one egg or two. The Gabar Goshawk (*M. gabar*), 11 to 14 inches, has an all-black color phase. It inhabits thickly wooded country, where it pursues small birds.

The Northern Goshawk (*Accipiter gentilis*), is found throughout northern temperate regions. The Black and White Goshawk (*A. melanoleucus*) of southern Africa, Henst's Goshawk (*A. hensti*) of Madagascar, Bürger's Goshawk (*A. buergersi*) of New Guinea, and Meyer's Goshawk (*A. meyerianus*) from nearby islands are all 17 to 24 inches, are brown, gray or black above, and white—usually darkly streaked or barred—below. They still-hunt or surprise prey.

Gundlach's Hawk (*A. gundlachi*), 16 to 19 inches, a rare bird native to Cuba, is bluish above, and barred brown below. Cooper's Hawk (*A. cooperii*) ranging from Canada to Mexico has similar plumage and preys chiefly on birds. From Mexico southward, the Bi-colored Hawk (*A. bicolor*) occurs. The tropical birds are smaller (13 to 15 inches) and are usually gray below with rufous thighs. The most southerly strains resemble Cooper's Hawk. The rare Gray-bellied Goshawk (*A. poliogaster*), 17 to 19 inches, of tropical South America is dark gray above, gray-white below.

Northern Goshawk (American race)

Small lightly built hawks with long toes, that enable them to grasp fast moving small birds, are found throughout the world except for the very cold regions. The Sharp-shinned Hawk (*A. striatus*) of the New World is similar in colour to Cooper's Hawk in North America, but very variable farther south. The Tiny Hawk (*A. superciliosus*), 9 to 12 inches, is found in tropical South America. The Eurasion Sparrow Hawk (*A. nisus*), 11 to 15 inches, is brown above and white barred with brown below. Males are brighter than females. The Madagascar Sparrow Hawk (*A. madagascariensis*) is similar to the Eurasian female, as is the Ovampo Sparrow Hawk (*A. ovampensis*), 9 to 11 inches, which inhabits open country in southern Africa. A forest-dwelling counterpart inhabiting eastern and southern Africa is the Rufous-breasted Sparrow Hawk (*A. rufiventris*). The Japanese Lesser Hawk (*A. gularis*), 9 to 12 inches, is much like the Eurasian species. Throughout southeast Asia occurs the brighter colored Besra Sparrow Hawk (*A. virgatus*), 9 to 12 inches. In Celebes, the Celebes Little Sparrow Hawk (*A. nanus*), 9 to 11 inches, dwells in lowland forest, and the Vinous-breasted Sparrow Hawk (*A. rhodogaster*), 11 to 13 inches, in the hills. Native to the Moluccas is the Gray-throated Sparrow Hawk (*A. erythrauchen*), 11 to 14 inches. The similar but shorter-tailed New Britain Sparrow Hawk

(*A. brachyurus*), 11 to 13 inches, is intermediate in appearance between the Gray-throated and the Collared Sparrow Hawk (*A. cirrhocephalus*), 10 to 13 inches, of Australia and New Guinea. A local rarity of Venezuela, Colombia and Ecuador is the Semi-collared Sparrow Hawk (*A. collaris*), 11 to 12 inches. Africa south of the Sahara has two small forest species, the Little Sparrow Hawk (*A. minullus*) and the Western Little Sparrow Hawk (*A. erythropus*), both 9 to 11 inches.

There are several species that have a heavier build and stronger, shorter legs and toes. Among them is the African Goshawk (*A. tachiro*), 14 to 17 inches, which is blackish above with chestnut barring below. The Chestnut-sided Goshawk (*A. castanilius*), 11 to 14 inches, is another occurring in tropical west Africa. The Gray-headed Goshawk (*A. poliocephalus*), 13 to 15 inches, is found on islands west of New Guinea. The New Britain Gray-headed Goshawk (*A. princeps*) is similar but larger. The Spot-tailed Goshawk (*A. trinotatus*), 12 inches, of Celebes is vinous below. The Chinese Goshawk (*A. soloensis*), 10 to 12 inches, is gray above, reddish or white below. The Shikra (*A. badius*), 11 to 14 inches, gray above, barred brown or rufous below, is found in southern Asia and Africa. The Nicobar Shikra (*A. butleri*), 11 to 13

Three phases of Gray or Variable Goshawk

Rufous-breasted Sparrow Hawk chasing Wheatear; eastern and southern Africa

inches, is paler above and more rufous below. The Levant Sparrow Hawk (*A. brevipes*), 13 to 15 inches, of the Black Sea region, is darker above. Frances's Sparrow Hawk (*A. francesii*), 11 to 13 inches, of Madagascar has faint gray bars below.

The Crested Goshawk (*A. trivirgatus*), 13 to 18 inches, found from India to Borneo, is gray above and has a black streak on its white throat. The Celebes Crested Goshawk (*A. griseiceps*), 13 to 15 inches, has a blue head and white underparts streaked with dark. The Black-mantled Goshawk (*A. melanochlamys*), 13 to 15 inches, black above and reddish-brown below, is a native of New Guinea. Closely related are the Pied Goshawk (*A. albogularis*), 13 to 16 inches, of the Solomons, the Black-throated Goshawk (*A. haplochrous*), 14 to 16 inches, of New Caldeonia, and the Fiji Goshawk (*A. rufitorques*), 13 to 16 inches, which is light gray above and reddish below and on it's collar. Another Solomon Islands native is the Imitator Hawk (*A. imitator*), 11 to 13 inches, which superficially resembles the Pied Goshawk. On New Britain, the Blue and Gray Sparrow Hawk (*A. luteoschistaceus*), 12 to 15 inches, has a slate-gray back and buffish underparts. The Molluccan species, Gray's Goshawk (*A. henicogrammus*), 15 to 19 inches, is dark gray above, and chestnut barred with white below. The White, Gray or Vinous Goshawk (*A. novae-*

Far right Lizard Buzzard; southern Africa (above) White-eyed Buzzard; India and Burma (below)

hollandiae), 13 to 20 inches, occurs in Australia, New Guinea and nearby islands. The Gray-throated Goshawk (*A. griseogularis*), 17 to 19 inches, occurs in the Molluccas. The Australian Goshawk (*A. fasciatus*), 13 to 20 inches, occurs from Christmas Island and Java to New Caledonia.

These species usually build tree nests, laying from two to six eggs; tropical species tend to have smaller clutches.

The Lizard Buzzard (*Kaupifalco monogrammicus*), 12 to 13 inches, is a hawk found in Africa south of the Sahara. It hunts lizards, snakes, rodents and, in some areas, birds. It lays one to three eggs in small tree-nests.

The Grasshopper Buzzard (*Butastur rufipennis*), 14 to 16 inches, found from Senegal to Somalia, is ginger-colored. It feeds mostly on insects. The White-eyed Buzzard (*B. teesa*), 15 to 17 inches, from India and Burma; the Rufous-winged Buzzard (*B. liventer*), 15 to 17 inches, from Thailand, Malaysia and Indonesia; and the Gray-faced Buzzard (*B. indicus*), 16 to 18 inches, which is found in China and Japan in summer, all still-hunt for insects, frogs and lizards.

Rough-legged Hawk; world-wide.

Buzzards

Many of the species commonly called hawks are actually buzzards of the genus *Buteo*. The buzzards are less specialized than other birds of prey. They are not as strong as some nor as fast as others, but are nevertheless a very successful group and are found throughout most of the world.

The Gray Hawk (*Buteo nitidus*), 15 to 17 inches, is gray with white barring below. It is found from Mexico to northern Argentina in fairly open country with scattered bushes and trees. It hunts in a hawklike manner—dashing low after birds, small mammals, reptiles and insects. The Roadside Hawk (*B. magnirostris*), 11 to 14 inches, is a brownish bird, pale below with brown bars, ranging from southern Mexico to northern Argentina. Its close relatives, Ridgway's Hawk (*B. ridgwayi*) of Hispaniola and the White-rumped hawk (*B. leucorrhous*), 14 to 15 inches, a mainly black bird found from western South America to southern Brazil, are also still-hunters. The Broad-winged Hawk (*B. platypterus*), 14 to 18 inches, of the United States and certain Caribbean Islands is brown above and gray or brown below spotted and barred with white. Like the Red-shouldered Hawk (*B. lineatus*), 16 to 20 inches, of the United States—a rufous bird with a distinctly barred blackish and white tail—the broad winged bird lives in wooded or swampy country, taking fish and amphibians in addition to the usual buzzard's fare. The Short-tailed Hawk (*B. brachyurus*), 15 to 17 inches, which is dark above and white below or all dark, is found from Florida to the southern Andes. The mountain forms are streaked with brown.

100

Red-tailed Hawk binding to
North American cacomistle

Common
Buzzard

Both the Red-backed Buzzard (*B. polyosoma*), 19 to 21 inches, and Gurney's Buzzard (*B. poecilochrous*), 20 to 22 inches, have several color phases. Females have brick-red backs, gray wings. Below they are often light with fine barring, or wholly dark. Males may be gray or black above and below. Sometimes they are white below, with some red on the back. Both species are Andean, Gurney's Buzzard having longer wings and being found north of Chile at high altitudes. The White-tailed Hawk (*B. albicaudatus*), 23 to 24 inches, a long-winged bird found in open country from the southern United States to Argentina, has reddish-brown shoulders and may be light or dark below with a broad, black subterminal band on the tail. It lives mostly on lizards and rodents. These

White-tailed Hawk;
southern U.S.
and South America.

buzzards are attracted to grass or cane fires, where they circle overhead on the look out for prey seeking to escape the flames.

The huge South American Gray Eagle Buzzard (*B. melanoleucus*), 22 to 31 inches, is gray above and on the breast. Strains from the Andes are white, finely barred with gray below, whereas those from low regions south of Paraguay are completely white underneath. This bird has very long wings and a short wedge-shaped tail, making its flight silhouette resemble that of a sea eagle. The Ferruginous Rough-legged Hawk (*B. regalis*), 24 to 26 inches, from the western United States and southern Canada is brown or rufous above and white below or, in another phase, all blackish. The Rough-legged Hawk (*B. lagopus*), 20 to 24 inches, is a variable bird that generally has much white on the head, chest and tail. It is found over sub-arctic regions. The last two species have leg feathers to the toes and live mainly on rodents. The Long-legged Buzzard (*B. rufinus*), 22 to 26 inches, is a bird with variable brown plumage and a rufous-brown tail, found from North Africa to central Asia. The Upland Buzzard (*B. hemilasius*), 24 to 27 inches, of central Asia is similar but has completely feathered legs. Both species are powerful enough to kill animals up to the size of a hare.

The Red-tailed Hawk (*B. jamaicensis*), 20 to 23 inches,

of North America, the Common or Steppe Buzzard (*B. buteo*), 19 to 22 inches, of Europe and Asia, and the South American Red-tailed Buzzard (*B. ventralis*), 19 to 21 inches, of Patagonia, inhabit hilly, wooded temperate regions. Their plumage varies from blackish-brown to buff, the tails usually red or brown with dark bars. The Mountain Buzzard (*B. oreophilus*), 16 to 18 inches, found at altitudes above 6,000 feet in eastern and southern Africa, is dark above, white marked with brown on the breast, and a rufous belly. The Madagascar Buzzard (*B. brachypterus*), 16 to 18 inches, is similar to the Mountain Buzzard, showing more white underneath, with shorter wings. Swainson's Hawk (*B. swainsoni*), 18 to 21 inches, of western North America, has a brown breast and is usually buff with dark bars below, but goes through an all-dark phase. Both phases have a gray tail barred with brown.

Two buzzards are found on Pacific islands. The brown Galapagos Buzzard (*B. galapagoensis*), 19 to 22 inches, is the tamest of the world's birds of prey. The Hawaiian Buzzard (*B. solitarius*), 15 to

Gray Hawk; Mexico and South America.

Roadside Hawk with anole lizard; Mexico and South America.

Harris' Hawk;
southwestern U.S.,
Mexico and
South America.

17 inches, is dark above with white on the head and on the breast, which is sometimes also marked with brown or buff. There is a dark brown phase.

The African Red-tailed Buzzard (*B. auguralis*), 16 to 18 inches, occurs over most of west Africa and the Sudan. It is usually brown above, on the head, and on the breast, and whitish with dark marks below. In eastern and southern Africa, the Augur Buzzard (*B. rufofuscus*), 19 to 22 inches, is a large buzzard with a short rufous tail. Usually black or gray above, it may be white, rufous or black below. In central and northern South America, the Zone-tailed Buzzard (*B. albonotatus*), 18 to 21 inches, is blackish with wide white bars on the tail.

Buzzards spend much time soaring, but usually kill by still-hunting or flying harrier- or hawk-fashion in search of prey which consists mostly of mammals up to rabbit size. Some hover when hunting open country or walk about on the ground. Most species are noisy. They generally nest in trees, but in hilly country they often use a rock ledge.

Harris' Hawk (*Parabuteo unicinctus*), 19 to 22 inches, is a reddish-brown or dark brown bird with powerful legs and feet. It occurs from the southwestern United States to south-

Black-faced Hawk, northern South America (*behind*) and White Hawk; Mexico to Boliva (*front*)

ern South America in dry bush country where it hunts in a hawklike manner for prey up to the size of small herons and rabbits. It lays three to five eggs. The Savannah Hawk (*Heterospizias meridionalis*), 20 to 24 inches long, is a long-legged South American bird, feeding mostly on snakes and lizards. It generally hunts from a perch a few feet above the ground. It is bright red and gray-brown. One or two eggs are laid in a tree nest.

The following birds are tropical buzzards, inhabiting forests or clumps of trees in low country in South and Central America. The Slate-colored Hawk (*Leucopternis schistacea*), 17 to 18 inches, has brown on the wings and a black tail with a white band and white tip. It lives in Colombia, Venezuela and northern Brazil. The Plumbeous Hawk (*L. plumbea*), 15 inches, of western Colombia and Ecuador is also slate gray with black wings and a black tail that has a white band. The Semi-plumbeous Hawk (*L. semiplumbea*) of Central America and western Colombia is also 15 inches in size and otherwise similar to the Plumbeous Hawk, except that it is white below. The White-browed Hawk (*L. kuhli*) of the Amazon, also 15 inches in size, is dark above and white on the brow, sides of the neck and below. The Black-faced Hawk (*L. melanops*), from the Guianas to the Amazon, is 16 inches in size and has a white head and underparts (excluding the face).

The Mantled Hawk (*L. polionota*), 19 to 21 inches, of southern Brazil and Paraguay is black above and on the upper half of the tail and white everywhere else. The White Hawk (*L. albicollis*), 19 to 23 inches, found from Mexico to Bolivia, is white with black on the wings and tail band. The Gray-backed Hawk (*L. occidentalis*), 19 inches, of western Ecuador is white below, streaked dark on the sides with a black band on the lower tail. The Barred Hawk (*L. princeps*), 18 to 20 inches, is a black bird with finely barred underparts that inhabits mountain forests from Costa Rica to Ecuador. These hawks are mostly still-hunters but can fly quickly among the branches of forest trees in pursuit of lizards, snakes, small mammals and slow-moving birds.

The Black-collared Fishing Hawk (*Busarellus nigricollis*), 19 to 21 inches, is found from Mexico to northern Argentina, generally in low-lying country subject to flooding. The undersides of its toes are furnished with spike-like scales similar to the Osprey's, for this bird lives mostly by snatching fish from the surface of the water. It will also eat crabs, small mammals and reptiles. It builds its nest in a tall tree, laying one or two eggs.

Crowned Eagle; South America

The Rufous Crab Hawk (*Buteogallus aequinoctialis*), 16 to 19 inches in size, appears in coastal swamp forests of northern and eastern South America. It is reddish-brown with some gray on the head and wings. Besides crabs, it will also take frogs and fish. The Common Black Hawk (*B. anthracinus*), 18 to 23 inches, inhabits wooded areas near water from the southern United States to northern South America. It has brown mottling on the wings and white near the wing tips. The Great Black Hawk (*B. urubitinga*), 20 to 25 inches, found from southern Mexico to northern Argentina, frequents wet areas, but is also found in dry regions. Both catch fish, frogs, lizards and snakes. The Great Black Hawk also takes small mammals and birds. These species nest in trees and lay one or two eggs.

The Solitary Eagle (*Harpyhaliaetus solitarius*), 27 to 29 inches, is a dark brown bird with a short crest, and a black tail with a white bar and tip. It is found from Mexico along the Andes to Peru. The Crowned Eagle (*H. coronatus*), 29 to 32 inches, is gray with a long crest, found from Bolivia to Argentina. Both species catch mammals up to the size of young deer.

Great Black Hawk;
Mexico and South America

Black-collared
Fishing Hawk;
Mexico and
South
America

Harpy Eagle with agouti;
Mexico and South America

Harpy Eagles

The Crested Eagle (*Morphnus guianensis*), 32 to 36 inches, inhabits tropical forests, from Honduras to northern Argentina. A slim, long-tailed, long-legged eagle, this bird is brownish-black above, gray or black on the chest, and white barred with rufous or black below. Its tail is black with ash-brown bars. This eagle preys mainly on mammals up to the size of a small monkey and often kills reptiles. It nests high up in huge forest trees and probably lays only one egg.

The Harpy Eagle (*Harpia harpyja*) grows 36 to 40 inches long. The female is, on the average, the world's most powerful eagle. Its hind claws are thicker—if not quite as long—as those of the largest carnivore, the Kodiak bear. It inhabits tropical forests from southern Mexico to northern Argentina. Unlike the previous species, the Harpy seldom soars. A female may weigh 18 pounds, yet can lift heavy prey in almost vertical ascent. It kills monkeys, sloths, and wild pigs, as well as large forest birds, such as macaws. Usually it chooses the largest tree in the vicinity for its nests and lays

Monkey-eating Eagle; Philippine Islands

one egg.

The New Guinea Harpy Eagle (*Harpyopsis novaeguineae*) grows 30 to 34 inches long. This large forest eagle often has orange-buff markings below. It preys on marsupial mammals and has been known to kill pigs. Its nesting habits are similar to those of the previous species.

The Monkey-eating Eagle (*Pithecophaga jefferyi*) of the Philippine Islands is 34 to 40 inches in size and is now found only on Mindanao and Luzon. It is the rarest eagle in the world—there are probably not more than fifty pairs surviving today. Almost as powerful as the Harpy, this huge forest eagle is known to kill monkeys and also large forest birds including hornbills. This eagle has a loud plaintive call. It lays two eggs and apparently breeds most years. It chooses the usual nest site of forest eagles, a tall tree. The Monkey-eating Eagle resembles the New Guinea Harpy Eagle in size and strength but has a longer beak and heavier, more powerful toes.

True Eagles

With one or two exceptions, all the birds described so far have the lower parts of their legs covered by scales. The following species, the true eagles, are feathered to the toes.

The Lesser Spotted Eagle (*Aquila pomarina*) of eastern Europe, southeast Asia and India is 24 to 26 inches in size and is a lightly built, long-winged brown bird—named for the two rows of white spots on the wings of its young. The young of the Greater Spotted Eagle (*A. clanga*), 26 to 29 inches, is even more heavily spotted but the adult is dark brown, generally with a white rump. It has a heavier build than has the Lesser Spotted, with a much broader wing tip visible in flight. Both birds are woodland species, often found near water. They prey on small mammals, reptiles, frogs and water birds. They are tree nesters, laying one to three eggs.

The Tawny Eagle (*A. rapax*) of Africa and Asia is 26 to 31 inches in size and is the world's most common eagle. It may be almost any shade of brown. Strains found in central Asia and eastern Europe are larger and are known as Steppe Eagles. They take a wide variety of prey ranging from eagle owls to flying ants, and they also eat carrion. They nest in trees, or sometimes on the ground or on rock ledges. They lay one or two eggs, occasionally three. The Imperial Eagle (*A. heliaca*), 31 to 33 inches, from the Iberian peninsula, eastern Europe and central Asia, has white patches on the upper back; the western strains have white shoulders. It usually lays two eggs in tree nests.

Spanish Imperial Eagle with
red squirrel; Eurasia

Wedge-tailed Eagle; Australia (*left*). (*Below*) Golden Eagle in flight seen from below; Northern Hemisphere.

The Golden Eagle (*A. chrysaetos*), 30 to 40 inches, is found in mountainous regions throughout the northern hemisphere. It may be any shade of brown, but is generally golden on the hind neck. Golden Eagles are very powerful birds; the largest in Asia regularly kill wolves and have been known to kill fairly large deer. They are fast enough to catch many kinds of large birds, but their most frequent prey is mammals up to the size of a hare. They build huge nests on trees or rock ledges. Eggs are usually two, occasionally one or three. Verreaux's Eagle (*A. verreauxi*), 32 to 35 inches, is a black eagle with a white back. It lives on mountains in eastern and southern Africa, preying on the Rock Hyrax. It generally lays its one or two eggs in a nest on a crag. The Wedge-tailed Eagle (*A. audax*), 34 to 40 inches, of Australia and Tasmania (where the largest birds occur) is a blackish-brown eagle preying on animals up to the size of small kangaroos. It also eats reptiles and carrion. It drives prey from cover by dropping sticks onto it from the air. Two eggs are laid in large tree nests. Gurney's Eagle (*A. gurneyi*), 26 to 30 inches, of western New Guinea is blackish with short wings and long tail.

Black Eagle with bird's nest;
India to Celebes.

Black Eagle and Forest Hawk-Eagles

The Indian Black Eagle (*Ictinaetus malayensis*), 25 to 29 inches, inhabits jungled hills from the Himalayas to Celebes. A lightly built bird with very long wings and tail, it is a most buoyant flier, soaring even in unfavorable weather conditions with scarcely a wing flap. It glides down to treetop level and snatches nests from the branches, eating both eggs and young birds. It also catches lizards and birds up to the size of small pheasants, as well as small mammals. It builds a large tree nest and usually lays only one egg.

The Mountain Hawk-Eagle (*Spizaetus nipalensis*), 26 to 34 inches, is found from Ceylon through southern India and the Himalayas, and as far north as Japan, where the largest individuals occur. Short-winged, long-tailed forest birds, they are brown above and fawn below with white bars. Some have long crests. They are still-hunters, preying on small mammals, young monkeys and small deer. They lay one egg in a nest in a forest tree. The Java Hawk-Eagle (*S. bartelsi*), 22 to 24 inches, is a blackish bird with a brownish band across the tail and white barring below. The Celebes Hawk-Eagle (*S. lanceolatus*), 22 to 25 inches, is black and brown above, rufous with black streaks on the chest, and barred brown

Ornate Hawk-Eagle;
Mexico and South America

and white below. It has a very short crest. The Philippine
Hawk-Eagle (S. *philippensis*), 25 to 27 inches, is similar
but has brown underparts. Blyth's Hawk-Eagle (S. *albon-
iger*), 20 to 23 inches, found from southern Burma to Sumatra and Borneo, is brownish-black above and white below. It is streaked on the breast and barred below with black.
A whitish band marks its tail, and a long crest adorns its
head. It inhabits almost the same area as Wallace's Hawk-
Eagle (S. *nanus*), 18 to 20 inches, which is brown above,
with head and underparts pinkish-buff, sometimes with dark
markings.

The Changeable Hawk-Eagle (S. *cirrhatus*), 22 to 32 inches,
occurs from northern India to Mindanao and Flores, where the
largest specimens occur. It may be all blackish or dark above
and white below, or the underparts may be streaked or all
brown. Most Indian birds possess a crest that specimens elsewhere lack. On sighting prey it sits motionless and erect with
its feathers drawn in tight, then it makes a sudden quick dash
at it. Its nesting habits are like those of the Mountain Hawk-
Eagle. Both species have an unusual call consisting of a series
of shrill piping notes.

Martial Eagle striking at guinea fowl; Africa south of the Sahara.

Large Forest Eagles

Cassin's Hawk-Eagle (*Spizaetus africanus*) of western Africa and the Congo forests is 22 to 24 inches in size and is black above, white below and has no crest. It catches arboreal animals such as squirrels and medium-sized birds. Little else is known about it. The Tyrant or Black Hawk-Eagle (*S. tyrannus*), 25 to 28 inches, is found in lowland forests from southern Mexico to northern Argentina. It is brownish-black with a long gray barred tail and white markings on the crest and underparts. The Ornate Hawk-Eagle (*S. ornatus*), 24 to 26 inches, is found throughout the same area. It is believed to attack small mammals and lizards, killing fewer birds than does the Tyrant Hawk Eagle. It frequently soars with wings held flat. As with all crested eagles, the position of the long crest indicates mood —bristling when the bird is anxious or aggressive. The Ornate Hawk-Eagle breeds in giant forest trees and lays one egg.

The Crowned Hawk-Eagle (*Stephanoaetus coronatus*), 32 to 39 inches, is found in forest regions and in wooded areas in Africa south of the Sahara. One of the world's most powerful eagles, it preys on small antelopes, monkeys, hyraxes, ground birds, and occasionally on snakes and lizards. It is less of a still-hunter than are most hawk eagles, often scouting for

114

prey by flying slowly and quietly among the trees. Like the Harpy Eagle, which has similar proportions, it can lift heavy prey almost vertically from the ground to a branch above. It generally lays two eggs in a huge nest in a tall tree. The beautiful, repetitive two-note piping call is the finest of all the birds of prey. It also utters a loud call during display.

The Black-and-Chestnut Eagle (*Oroaetus isidori*), 25 to 29 inches, is black above and on its long crest, head and thighs. It is reddish-brown below and has a gray tail with a broad black tip. It inhabits mountain forests in western South America from Venezuela to Argentina. It hunts monkeys, squirrels and other small to medium-sized animals, sometimes killing porcupines. It lays one egg in a tree-nest usually growing on a precipitous slope.

The Martial Eagle (*Polemaetus bellicosus*), 32 to 38 inches, is a long-winged, short-crested species inhabiting savannah and open wooded country in Africa south of the Sahara. It has long legs and toes, adaptations for clutching medium-sized birds such as francolins or guinea fowl in flight. It often spots prey while soaring high in the air, then sets off on a long fast glide in chase. Indeed, it spends a good deal of time on the wing, and when not hunting frequently soars for hours very high in the sky. It also kills small antelopes, hyraxes and takes poultry and goats. It builds a large nest in a tree, and lays only one egg.

Crowned Hawk-Eagle; Africa south of the Sahara.

European and Asian race

African race

Bonelli's Eagle *or* African Hawk-Eagle

Hawk-Eagles

The Long-crested Hawk-Eagle (*Lophoaetus occipitalis*), 20 to 22 inches, is found in Africa south of the Sahara in farmlands, lightly-forested areas, and grassland with scattered trees. It is fairly tame and still-hunts for rodents, reptiles and insects. It nests in a tree, and lays one or two eggs.

The Black-and-White Hawk-Eagle (*Spizastur melanoleucus*), 21 to 24 inches, is black above and on the crest, and white on the head and below. It inhabits forests from southern Mexico to Argentina, preying on small mammals, birds and reptiles.

The Booted Eagle (*Hieraetus pennatus*), 19 to 25 inches, may be all brown or brown above and lighter below. It inhabits open forests, often in the dry, rocky hill country of southern Europe and northern Africa. Its range extends to central Asia and India. It often nests in small trees. The Little Eagle (*H. morph-*

noides) of New Guinea and Australia is 17 to 22 inches and is similar to the Booted Eagle, except that it has a more pronounced crest which, with the top of the head, is blackish in color. It takes more mammals than does the Booted Eagle and also kills reptiles. Ayres' Hawk-Eagle (*H. dubius*), 19 to 21 inches, is found from Togo and Ethiopia to South Africa. It is dark brown above and white with dark marks below. It catches birds and squirrels. Bonelli's or the African Hawk-Eagle (*H. fasciatus*), 26 to 31 inches, is found in southern Europe, southern Asia, the island of Flores and most of Africa. It inhabits rocky hills in dry areas. It is able to catch large birds and mammals up to the size of small antelopes. It nests on rock ledges or in trees; two eggs are usual. The Rufous-bellied Hawk-Eagle (*H. kienerii*), 19 to 24 inches, is black above, white on the throat and breast, and reddish below. It is found from southern and eastern India to Celebes. Wahlberg's Eagle (*H. wahlbergi*), 22 to 24 inches, is a long-winged eagle, which is all brown, or brown above and light below. Found over most of Africa south of the Sahara, it is not a strong bird.

Long-crested Hawk-Eagle; Africa south of the Sahara.

Laughing Falcon with coral snake; Mexico and South America

Forest Falcons

The Laughing Falcon (*Herpetotheres cachinnans*), 17 to 20 inches, is found from Mexico to Argentina, both in forests and in dry open country, anywhere where snakes, their main prey, are numerous. Unlike most falcons, these are short-winged birds with fairly long tails. They are normally still-hunters and are noisy birds, especially in the evening. They lay one egg in a hole in a tree or cliff, or occasionally in the abandoned nest of another bird of prey.

The Collared Forest Falcon (*Micrastur semitorquatus*), 18 to 24 inches, is also found from Mexico to Argentina. A short-winged, long-tailed bird, it is not a strong flier but is able to glide rapidly through forest trees and to move quickly both among the branches and on the ground. It catches fairly large birds, often larger than itself. Traylor's Forest Falcon (*M. buckleyi*) from Ecuador is 16 to 18 inches in size and similar to the Collared Forest Falcon—except that it has brown on its feathers. It is also comparatively smaller, with much smaller legs and feet. The Slate-backed Forest Falcon (*M. miran-dollei*), found from Costa Rica to Peru and the mouth of the Amazon, is 17 to 18 inches in size. It also resembles the Col-

118

Collared Forest Falcon;
Mexico and South America

lared Forest Falcon except for its slate-gray back and lack of a white collar. The Barred Forest Falcon (*M. ruficollis*), 12 to 15 inches, is found from Mexico to Argentina in mountains and lowland forests. A very variable species, it is usually closely barred white and blackish below and gray, reddish or almost any shade of brown above. The tail of the female generally has three white bars above, while the tail of the male has only two. The Plumbeous Forest Falcon (*M. plumbeus*), 12 to 14 inches, from Ecuador and southwestern Colombia, is similar to the Barred Forest Falcon but has only one tail band. Nothing is known of the breeding habits of forest falcons except that some nest in tall trees.

The Yellow-throated Caracara (*Daptrius ater*), 16 to 18 inches, is a greenish-black bird with a white band across the tail and bare yellow skin on the face. It occurs in the forests of the Amazon and its tributaries. The Red-throated Caracara (*D. americanus*), 16 to 24 inches, occurs in forests from southern Mexico to southern Brazil, where the largest members of the species occur. It is black above and on the breast and white below. The bare skin on the face and throat is red. Both species

119

Crested or Common Caracara;
southern U.S., Mexico
and South America

eat fruit and catch insects, raiding wasps nests and catching
large beetles. They also kill small vertebrates that are not
difficult to catch. They nest in high forest trees and lay two
to three eggs.

Carrion Hawks

The Common Caracara (*Polyborus plancus*), 20 to 26 inches,
is found from the southern United States to Tierra del Fuego. A
bird of open country, it eats almost anything, spending much
time on the ground, running rapidly about in quest of food.
It is very noisy and has a loud rattling call. It may rob other
birds of food, attacking individuals up to its own size if they
are injured or sick. It nests in trees and lays two or three eggs.

The Carunculated Caracara (*Phalcoboenus carunculatus*),
19 to 21 inches, is a black bird with white streaking below and
white on the rump, vent and tail-tip. It has a bare orange or
red throat and face, which is very wrinkled. It is found in
Colombia and Ecuador. The Mountain Caracara (*P. megalo-
pterus*) of Peru, Bolivia and northern Chile is 19 to 21 inches in

Forster's Caracara;
Falkland Islands.

Red-throated Caracara;
Mexico and South America.

size and has a black breast and white underparts. The White-throated Caracara (*P. albogularis*) of Chile and Argentina is 19 to 21 inches in size and is entirely white below. Forster's Caracara (*P. australis*) of the Falkland Islands and islands near Tierra del Fuego is 23 to 25 inches in size and black with fine white streaks, rufous on the abdomen and thighs. These closely related birds are normally found in the Andes in high treeless areas. Forster's Caracara lives in similar areas near the sea. They are sociable birds, feeding mostly on carrion and invertebrates. They breed on cliffs, laying two to four eggs.

The Chimango Caracara (*Milvago chimango*) of southern South America is 15 to 16 inches in size, rufous brown above, white on the rump and brown, mottled buffish-white below. From Panama to northern Argentina, excepting the Andes, is the range of the Yellow-headed Caracara (*M. chimachima*), which is 15 to 18 inches. Both species frequent lightly wooded or open country, including seashores. Usually seen pecking on the ground, they are omnivorous like the crows and rooks. They build nests in trees, bushes or on the ground and usually lay three eggs.

Yellow-headed Caracara;
Central and South America.

121

Brown Falcon;
Australia and
New Guinea.

Spot-winged Falcon;
Argentina.

Fielden's Falconet;
southeast Asia.

122

Pygmy Falcons

The Spot-winged Falcon (*Spizapteryx circumcinctus*), 11 to 12 inches, is short-winged and inhabits open woodland in parts of northern Argentina. It is said to prey mainly on birds. Its nesting habits are unrecorded.

The Red-thighed Falconet or Pygmy Falcon (*Microhierax caerulescens*), 5½ to 6½ inches (see page 4), occurs from northern India to Vietnam. The Black-legged Falconet (*M. fringillarius*), 5½ to 6 inches, is black above and on the thighs, white on the chest and rufous below. It occurs from the Malay peninsula to Bali, and in southern Borneo. The Pied Falconet (*M. melanoleucus*), 6 to 7 inches, is black above and white on the forehead, eyestripe and below. It occurs from Assam to southern China. The White-headed or Bornean Falconet (*M. latifrons*) of northern Borneo, which is 6 inches in size, is illustrated on page 38. The Philippine Falconet (*M. erythrogonys*), 6 to 7 inches, is greenish-black above and on the thighs, and white below and on the sides of the neck and head.

Fielden's Falconet (*Poliohierax insignis*), 10 to 11 inches, has a longer, rounder tail than do other pygmy falcons, and the female has a red head. It is found from Burma to Cambodia. The African Pygmy Falcon (*P. semitorquatus*), 7½ inches, found in dry areas in southern and eastern Africa, is grey above and white below. The female is chestnut on the back. Usually seen in pairs, these birds prey mostly on insects and lizards. The Brown Falcon (*Falco berigora*) of Australia and New Guinea, 15 to 18 inches, is very variable in coloring.

In spite of their small size, pygmy falcons can kill birds up to the size of a small thrush. They also take small mammals and large insects. They nest in holes in trees, laying three to four eggs.

Kestrels or Sparrow Hawks

The White-eyed Kestrel (*F. rupicoloides*), 13 to 14 inches, of eastern and southern Africa is a brown, heavily barred bird confined to dry bush country with scattered trees. It is more of a still-hunter than is the Common Kestrel because it is a less efficient flier. It lays three to five eggs in an old nest of another bird, most often that of a Cape Rook. The Fox Kestrel (*F. alopex*), 14 to 15 inches, is found on rocky hills in dry country from Ghana to the Sudan and Ethiopia. It is a long-winged, long-tailed chestnut bird that feeds mainly on grasshoppers and small lizards. It nests in crevices in cliffs. The Common Kestrel (*F. tinnunculus*), 12 to 14 inches, is found over most of Europe, Africa and Asia, except in high arctic, extreme desert and heavily forested regions. Because it is the expert at hovering flight it can exploit the rodent population of the open country and is therefore more successful than any other bird of prey. For the same reason, it is the most numerous species. It eats small birds, lizards, frogs and worms. The male is illustrated on the opposite page. The female resembles the White-eyed Kestrel but has dark eyes. The species nests in abandoned nests of other birds, in hollow trees or on cliff ledges. It usually lays four or five eggs. The Madagascar Kestrel (*F. newtoni*), 10 to 11 inches, which lives on the Comoro and Aldabra Islands as well as Madagascar occurs in two color phases. One is light rufous above streaked with black, and whitish below. The other is dark rufous above and below, heavily streaked with black. The Mauritius Kestrel (*F. punctatus*), 11 to 13 inches, now probably the rarest bird of prey, resembles a female Common Kestrel but is white below spotted with black or rufous. It has six bars on the tail. The Seychelles Kestrel (*F. araea*),

Gray Kestrel; Africa

Common Sparrow
Hawk or Kestrel;
Eurasia and Africa.

9 to 10 inches, resembles a tiny male Common Kestrel but is unspotted below and has more bars on the tail. The Moluccan Kestrel (*F. moluccensis*), 11 to 13 inches, is a pale chestnut bird, heavily spotted and streaked with black throughout. The male is distinguished by one band on a blue-gray tail, whereas the female has several. The Nankeen Kestrel (*F. cenchroides*), 11 to 12 inches, of Australia and the highlands of New Guinea resembles the Common Kestrel, but both sexes tend to be amber-brown where the Common Kestrel is rufous-brown. In New Guinea, both sexes resemble male Common Kestrels. Behavior and nesting habits are also similar to those of the Common Kestrel. The Lesser Kestrel (*F. naumanni*), 11 to 12 inches, is an insectivorous species found in southern Europe and central Asia in summer, migrating south in winter. Males resemble Common Kestrels but have unspotted red backs, Females resemble small female Common Kestrels, but both sexes have white claws. They catch much of their prey in the air, are very sociable and breed in colonies in cliffs and buildings.

Male American Sparrow Hawk hovering;
North and South America.

The American Kestrel or Sparrow Hawk (*F. sparverius*), 9 to 12 inches, breeds from southern Alaska and Newfoundland, south to Patagonia. It is lightly built, like the Lesser Kestrel, but with more of the Common Kestrel's habits. Although it prefers an insect diet, it will take small rodents, birds, snakes and lizards. Females are banded reddish-brown and dark brown on the wings and tail. The male bird is illustrated on page 125. Nesting habits are the same as those of the Common Kestrel.

The Gray Kestrel (*F. ardosiaceus*), 13 to 14 inches, is found

Merlin or Pigeon Hawk
hunting; Northern Hemisphere

in open woodland in much of Africa. A heavy, stocky bird, it is mainly a still-hunter. It lays three to five eggs in a hole in a tree or in an abandoned nest. Dickinson's Kestrel (*F. dickinsoni*), 11 to 12 inches, is a lighter gray bird but with blackish wings and back. It is found from Tanzania to Mozambique and Angola where it occurs in low-lying country and is often seen in small parties. It pursues locusts in the air and catches lizards on the ground. It lays two or three eggs in the crown of a palm tree. The Barred Kestrel (*F. zoniventris*) of Madagascar, of which little is known, is 12 to 13 inches in size. It is a gray bird, white below with brown bars.

The Red-footed Falcon (*F. vespertinus*), 11 to 12 inches, found from eastern Europe to eastern Asia in summer, migrates to Africa in winter. The male is gray with rufous thighs and vent. The female is rufous on the head and below, pale gray barred with dark gray above. Usually seen in flocks, these birds hawk insects high in the air. They breed communally in old nests of the crow family and lay four or five eggs.

The Red-headed Merlin (*F. chiquera*), 11 to 13 inches, is found in open country in southern Africa and India. A fast, strong hunter, it catches birds up to the size of small doves and quail. It lays two to four eggs in tree nests. The Merlin or Pigeon Hawk (*F. columbarius*), 10 to 13 inches, is found throughout the Northern Hemisphere. A fast, low-level hunter in open country, it catches small birds and large insects. It lays four or five eggs in an old nest on the ground, or in holes in trees or stream banks.

Red-headed Merlin; southern Africa and India.

127

Little Falcon pursuing Parakeet; Australia.

Hobbys

The Little Falcon (*F. longipennis*) of Australia, Timor, Flores and Ceram is 11 to 13 inches in size and is blue above, rufous on the hind neck, and duller below. A strong, dashing little bird, it hunts in open or lightly wooded country especially near water, where it catches birds as they fly in to drink. It nests high in a tree and lays three eggs. The Oriental Hobby (*F. severus*), 11 to 13 inches, occurs from the central Himalayas to the Solomon Islands. It is black above and on the head and reddish-chestnut below. It catches small birds, bats and insects over wooded country, often hunting at dawn and dusk. It breeds in an old tree-nest or on a rock ledge, usually laying two eggs. The African Hobby (*F. cuvieri*), 10 to 12 inches, is found in open and lightly wooded country in central, eastern and south-eastern Africa. It is grayish-black above, rufous below, with white on the cheeks and chin. Although its chief prey are large flying insects, it occasionally takes small birds on the wing. It breeds in an old nest in a tall tree. The European Hobby

(*F. subbuteo*), 12 to 14 inches, breeds in central Asia in summer, migrating to Africa and southern Asia in winter. In hawks high in the air for small birds, insects and bats. It is extremely fast, frequently overtaking swifts in flight. Seen from below, it resembles a huge swift. It usually lays three or four eggs in an abandoned crow's nest. The Bat Falcon (*F. rufigularis*), 9 to 12 inches, found from Mexico to northern Argentina, is tiny but very strong and fast. It can catch almost any small bird or large insect in the air. It takes the largest swifts by getting above them and diving. In the speed of its dive, this hobby has no rivals among the smaller raptors. It lays two or three eggs, usually in a cavity in a tree.

Eleanora's Falcon (*F. eleanorae*), 14 to 15 inches, is common to islands in the Mediterranean. It resembles a large long-tailed hobby, except that it lacks reddish coloring below. Some birds are blackish throughout. They feed mostly on other birds. Because their prey is most plentiful at the time of the autumn migration, they breed in the fall, laying two or three eggs on a cliff ledge. The Sooty Falcon (*F. concolor*) of eastern Africa and Madagascar, 12 to 13 inches, is a blackish-gray bird with dark brown wings found in woodlands, as well as in deserts and on islands. It preys on migrant birds, as well as bats and insects. It lays three eggs among rocks.

Eurasian Hobby at rest and in flight

Gyr Falcon—Iceland race

Large Falcons

The Black Falcon (*F. subniger*), 17 to 19 inches, is a blackish-brown bird, generally found in open or lightly wooded country inland in Australia, where it preys on medium-sized birds. It lays three or four eggs in an old nest of another bird. The New Zealand Falcon (*F. novaezeelandiae*), 15 to 18 inches, is blackish-brown above, buffish-white with brown streaks below, and reddish on the thighs and undertail coverts. Its prey consists of small birds, rodents, lizards and insects. It usually lays three eggs on a rocky ledge. The Aplomado Falcon (*F. femoralis*), 13 to 17 inches, occurs from the southern

Saker Falcon;
Eurasia

United States to Tierra del Fuego. It is gray above and white below, with heavy black bars on the underparts and buffy-orange on the thighs, undertail, and sometimes on the breast and collar. It catches large insects, small birds, rodents, small snakes and lizards. It builds a low tree nest in dry country.

The Gray Falcon (*F. hypoleucos*), 12 to 16 inches, inhabits the dry and mountainous regions of Australia. It preys mainly on small marsupials, reptiles and birds. The Laggar Falcon (*F. jugger*), of India, 15 to 17 inches, is ash-brown above with a dull rufous crown, and whitish below with dark streaks from the lower breast downward, with brown flanks and thighs. It is an agile flier and can catch birds up to the size of partridges. The Lanner Falcon (*F. biarmicus*), 15 to 18 inches, is found in southeastern Europe and most of the drier parts of Africa. It catches a large variety of birds and also kills rodents and lizards. It nests on a rock ledge or in abandoned tree-nests.

The Prairie Falcon (*F. mexicanus*), 16 to 19 inches, inhabits

Lanner Falcon

Europe and Africa

Gray Falcon; Australia.

dry open country in the western United States, southwestern Canada and Mexico. Speckled on the breast, it is wholly brown above. It preys on birds and rodents. It usually lays five eggs in a hollow or in a large deserted nest on a cliff. The Saker Falcon (*F. cherrug*) of southeastern Europe and central Asia, which is 18 to 23 inches in size, migrates to Africa and India in winter. It kills large birds—up to the size of the Imperial Eagle. It lays three to five eggs in a tree-nest or sometimes on a cliff ledge.

'Peale's Falcon', a race
of the Peregrine
Falcon; islands
off the west
coast of North America

Gyr and Peregrines

The Gyr Falcon (*F. rusticolus*) of the Arctic regions is 20 to 23 inches in size. It has several color phases, varying from clear white with a few dark marks to almost completely black. Usually the lightest birds occur in the far north and the darkest farthest south. The Gyrs are the largest, heaviest falcons and have the broadest wings. Very fast in level flight, they pursue ptarmigans, auks, waterfowl, waders and occasionally gulls and Arctic Hares. They feed largely on lemmings — when these are abundant. They usually lay four eggs often in the deserted nest of a raven on a cliff ledge. Because of their speed, these birds were, and still are, a favorite of falconers.

The Taita Falcon (*F. fasciinucha*), 11 to 13 inches, occurs in the drier parts of eastern Africa. Its chestnut underparts extend to the nape and it has the build of a tiny peregrine. It catches pigeons and smaller birds after a low-level chase. Its nesting habits are unknown. The Orange-breasted Falcon (*F. deiroleucos*), 13 to 15 inches, is found from Mexico to Argentina. It is similar to the Taita but has a black area on the lower breast and has a dark nape. It is even more peregrine-like in build, and presumably hunts medium-

Barbary Falcon: north Africa and Asia.

Peregrine Falcon in flight

sized birds. Little is recorded about this bird or about Klein-schmidt's Falcon (*F. kreyenborgi*), which is 15 to 17 inches in size, and which is hobby-like in the shape of its wings and tail but resembles a pale peregrine in color and build (except the head which is buff like that of a Lanner). It inhabits southern Argentina and Chile, where it breeds on rock ledges. The Peregrine Falcon (*F. peregrinus*), 13 to 19 inches, is found throughout the temperate zones, except on high mountains. It is a heavily built bird which enables it to dive at speeds of up to 200 miles an hour. Ducks, pigeons, waders, sea birds and small birds are its usual prey. Large birds are generally struck behind the head or upper wing with the hind claws as the falcon shoots by. Small birds are seized with the claws. Plumage varies in differ-ent parts of the world: birds from the west coast of North America are very dark, tropical birds usually have black heads, and desert birds—known as Barbary Falcons—are small and pale. All lay two to four eggs on a cliff ledge, building, abandoned tree-nest, or occasionally, on the ground. They may also nest on high buildings in cities.

133

Barn and Bay Owls

The Barn Owl (*Tyto alba*), 11 to 16 inches, is found world-wide in temperate regions where winters are not severe—as well as in the tropics except deserts and dense forests. The plumage is very variable. Barn Owls live almost entirely on rodents, so are beneficial to man. Their eyes are rather small for a nocturnal bird, but their ears take up almost the whole length of the skull. Thus, the prey is located almost entirely by sound. The call is an eerie shriek, and hissing, snoring, and chuckling notes are also uttered. Long wings allow this owl to glide silently over meadows or woodland country. Its numbers depend on the abundance of rodents, and when these are plentiful Barn Owls have been known to lay twice in one year. There are normally four to six eggs, laid in buildings, hollow trees, holes in cliffs or abandoned nests of other birds. The Grass Owl (*T. capensis*), 13 to 16 inches, found in southern Africa, parts of southeast Asia and Australia in grassland, is generally darker above than the Barn Owl. The tiny Madagascar Grass Owl (*T. soumagnei*), 10 inches, is very dark in color. The large Celebes Barn Owl (*T. rosenbergii*), 15 to

Barn Owl—light-
and dark-breasted form:
world-wide.

19 inches, is equally dark. Of the same size is the Masked Owl (*T. novaehollandiae*), of Tasmania. Females are over twice the weight of males and are able to catch rabbits, rat-kangaroos and ring-tailed opossums. Individuals from mainland Australia are smaller. This species lays only two or three eggs. The Sooty Owl (*T. tenebricosa*), 12 to 14 inches, is spotted dark brown above and light below in Australia, and dark brown throughout in New Guinea. The New Britain Barn Owl (*T. aurantia*), and the Minahassa Barn Owl (*T. inexspectata*) of Celebes, are both 10 to 12 inches in size and are brown with typical barn owl markings above.

The Bay Owl (*Phodilus badius*), 10 inches, lives in forests from central India to Borneo and Java. It spends the day in a hole in a tree. It is very sluggish, moreso even than the Barn Owl. It lays two to four eggs. Food is less specialized than is the Barn Owl's, and it will eat rodents, small birds, lizards, frogs and beetles. The call notes resemble a mixture of those of barn, scops and wood owls. The Congo Bay Owl (*P. prigoginei*), a darker bird with smaller feet, was not discovered until 1951.

Masked Owl (female); Tasmania

Bay Owl

135

White-faced Scops Owl; southern Africa.　　Eurasian Scops Owl

Scops and Screech Owls

The Scops Owl (*Otus scops*), 6½ to 8 inches, is found in tropical and warmer temperate parts of the Old World, anywhere where cover is sufficient. At night their call betrays their presence. Their food consists almost entirely of insects. They nest in holes. The Mountain Scops Owl (*O. spilocephalus*), 7 to 9 inches, occurs up to 7,000 feet from the Himalayas to Borneo. Its back is spotted. The Andaman Scops Owl (*O. balli*), 8 inches, has a dark-reddish back.

The Reddish Scops Owl (*O. rufescens*) of Malaya, Sumatra, Java and Borneo is orange-brown with pale eyebrows and forehead. In Celebes, the Sunda Islands and Moluccas, the Celebes Scops Owl (*O. manadensis*), 7½ to 9 inches, occurs. The Flores Scops Owl (*O. alfredi*), 7½ inches, is orange-brown with white markings. A similar owl, the Mentaur Scops Owl (*O. umbra*), 6½ inches, lives in the islands off Sumatra. The Palau Scops Owl (*O. podarginus*), 8½ inches, and

Screech Owl—dark and light phases; North America

the Wiak Scops Owl (*O. beccarii*) of the Scouten Islands off New Guinea, are both heavily barred. The Flammulated Owl (*O. flammeolus*) of the Rocky Mountains from British Columbia to southern Mexico is 6 inches in size. The Russet Scops Owl (*O. rutila*) of Madagascar and the Comoros and Pemba Islands is 7 to 9 inches in size, and chestnut-brown, or russet above and gray and brown below. In western Africa, the Cinnamon Scops Owl (*O. icterorhynchus*), 7 to 8 inches, is smaller. A smaller species (*O. ireneae*), grayer in color, was discovered in eastern Africa as recently as 1965.

Many species take more rodents, small birds and lizards. The White-faced Scops Owl (*O. leucotis*) of Africa south of Gambia and the central Sudan is 8 to 10 inches in size. The White-fronted Scops Owl (*O. sagittatus*), 10 to 11½ inches, is found from southern Burma to Malaya. The Giant Scops Owl (*O. gurneyi*), 12 inches, is known only from Mindanao and Marinduque in the Philippines. The Collared Scops Owl

137

(*O. bakkamoena*), 7 to 9½ inches, from Muscat in Arabia to Japan and Java is similar to the Screech Owl but browner. The Rajah Scops Owl (*O. brookei*) of Borneo, Sumatra and Java is 9 inches in size and is like a Collared but has more white in its plumage. The Lesser Sunda Scops Owl (*O. silvicola*), 10 inches, is similar to the Collared. The Screech Owl (*O. asio*), 7 to 9 inches, is common in the United States and parts of southern and western Canada. The Whiskered Screech Owl (*O. trichopsis*), 7 inches, occurs from the Arizona canyons to Honduras. The Pacific Screech Owl (*O. cooperi*), 8 inches, occurs in low, dry country from southern Mexico to Costa Rica. The Spix Screech Owl (*O. choliba*), 7 to 8 inches, from Costa Rica to northern Argentina, is finely barred below. The Puerto Rican Screech Owl (*O. nudipes*), 8 to 10 inches, lacks the ear tufts of the other screech owls. It has bare legs, as has the Cuban Bare-legged Owl (*O. lawrencii*), 8 inches. The Bearded Screech Owl (*O. barbarus*) of southern Mexico and Guatemala, and the Dark-crowned Screech Owl (*O. robor-*

Akun Eagle Owl;

Crested Owl; Mexico to South America

western Africa

atus) of Ecuador and Peru have white collars. The Tawny-bellied Screech Owl (*O. watsonii*), 8 to 9 inches, found from Colombia to Argentina, is dark above and orange-rufous with dark marks below. The Brazilian Black-capped Screech Owl (*O. atricapillus*) is another dark species. The Vermiculated Screech Owl (*O. guatemalae*), 8 to 9 inches, found from Mexico to Bolivia, is very dark below. The Rufescent Screech Owl (*O. ingens*), 9 to 11 inches, is similar but has no ear tufts. It occurs from Colombia to Bolivia, as does the White-throated Screech Owl (*O. albogularis*), 11 inches. The Bare-shanked Screech Owl (*O. clarkii*) occurs in Panama and Costa Rica.

The Maned Owl (*Jubula lettii*), 11 inches, found from Sierra Leone to western Kenya, is rare, as is the Crested Owl (*Lophostrix cristata*), 17 inches, from southern Mexico to the Amazon.

Eagle and Great Horned Owls
Nearly cosmopolitan in distribution, the owls of the genus *Bubo* are large sized fierce predators, diurnal as well as noctur-

Maned Owl; central Africa

nal in their habits. One relatively weak exception is the Akun Eagle Owl (*Bubo leucostrictus*) of west Africa, which is mainly insectivorous, catching cockroaches on the wing. Fraser's Eagle Owl (*B. poensis*), 14 to 18 inches, occurs in western African forests. It has an orange-yellow face, is brown above and white, finely barred with brown, below. A subspecies in the Amani forest in Tanzania is heavily marked with brown below. The call of these birds is a long series of short, deep hoots. The Malay Eagle Owl (*B. sumatrana*), 16 to 18 inches, occurs from southern Burma to Borneo and Bali. It is rather like the Fraser's but has longer barred ear tufts. The Forest Eagle Owl (*B. nipalensis*), 20 to 24 inches, is found over most of India, Ceylon, and east to Vietnam. It is not unlike a large, heavily-marked Malay bird. It kills small mammals including flying squirrels, birds, snakes and lizards. The Dusky Eagle Owl (*B. coromandus*), 19 to 22 inches, lives in small woods and groves from India to Malaysia. It is grayish-brown mottled with white, and has deep yellow eyes. It preys upon crows in their nests at night.

The Milky Eagle Owl (*B. lacteus*) of Africa south of the Sahara is 21 to 23 inches in size and is very nocturnal, almost torpid by day. Shelley's Eagle Owl (*B. shelleyi*), 24 inches, the large eagle owl of west African forests, is dark-eyed, barred dark brown and white. The Spotted Eagle Owl (*B. africanus*), 13 to 17 inches, inhabits rocky country over most of Africa and southern Arabia. It is mottled white, gray and black throughout, with brown markings below. The Cape Eagle Owl (*B. capensis*), 19 to 21 inches, is found on high mountains in southern and eastern Africa. The Great Eagle Owl (*B. bubo*) of Europe, Asia and north Africa is 17 to 30 inches in size and varies in size according to region. The bird illustrated on the opposite page is a small desert form from Arabia. The largest birds occur in Siberia and Turkestan. All the eagle owls kill mammals, birds nearly their own size, reptiles and insects. The call of these species is a low, double hoot. The Great Horned Owl (*B. virginianus*), 18 to 23 inches, occurs in the New World from central Alaska and Labrador to the Straits of Magellan. Rabbits

Great Horned Owl; New World (*top*).
Desert Eagle Owl; Arabian race (*center*).
Milky Eagle Owl (*below*).

Brown Fish Owl;
Asia

are its favorite food, but it also attacks skunks, porcupines, birds and snakes. Its most frequent call is a series of five to seven low hoots. Eagle owls lay one to three eggs on rock ledges or in crevices, in abandoned nests of other birds, or in depressions in the ground in flat, treeless country. The Philippine Eagle Owl (*B. philippensis*), 17 inches, is little known. Dark orange above, paler below and streaked dark brown throughout, it resembles a fish owl.

Fish Owls and the Snowy Owl

Blakiston's Fish Owl (*Ketupa blakistoni*) of northeastern Asia is 18 to 23 inches, pale-colored with brown streaks and reddish-brown bars. It is feathered to the toes, which prevents frostbite. The Tawny Fish Owl (*K. flavipes*), 19 to 21 inches, occurs from the lower Himalayas to southern China and Vietnam. It is pale rufous-brown, streaked with gray-brown. The lower legs

Pel's Fishing Owl;
Africa below the Sahara

are feathered half way down. In the next two species, the lower legs are completely bare. The Malay Fish Owl (*K. ketupa*), 17 to 18 inches, found from Burma to Borneo, is pale amber-brown with darker brown streaks. The Brown Fish Owl (*K. zeylonensis*), 19 to 21 inches, occurs from southern Turkey to southern China. These owls are found in trees near fresh water up to 7,000 feet. In addition to fish they eat small mammals, birds, reptiles, crabs and insects. They normally lay two eggs in a hole.

Pel's Fishing Owl (*Scotopelia peli*), 21 to 24 inches, inhabits Africa below the Sahara. The Rufous Fishing Owl (*S. ussheri*) is more variable in color but less heavily barred. It is confined to west African rain forests, as is Bouvier's Fishing Owl (*S. bouvieri*), 15 to 17 inches, which is dark above and white and heavily streaked below. These species appear to feed almost entirely on fish. They lay four eggs.

The Snowy Owl (*Nyctea scandiaca*), 21 to 24 inches, lives in

Snowy Owl; Arctic.

barren Arctic regions but flies south in winter to occupy moors and coastal marshes. Although it can kill prey up to the size of geese and hares, its main food in the Arctic is the lemming. When lemmings are scarce, it may not attempt to breed, but when they are plentiful up to ten eggs may be laid in a depression on a rise in the ground.

Pygmy Owls and the Elf Owl

Strong for their size, Pygmy Owls hunt a variety of prey, including lizards, snakes, small mammals and other birds. They are active both in the dark and the daylight, often boast musical calls, and nest in tree holes, laying three to five eggs. The Eurasian Pygmy Owl (*Glaucidium passerinum*), 6½ inches, inhabits mountains with coniferous forests. The Collared Owlet (*G. brodie*), 6 to 6½ inches, which has a brown and a red phase, is indigenous to southeast Asia. The Jungle Owlet (*G. radia-*

144

tum), 6½ to 7½ inches, inhabits Indian jungles. The Barred Owlet (*G. cuculoides*), 8 to 10 inches, occurs in the Himalayas, China and Java.

Africa has four pygmy owls—the Pearl-spotted Owlet (*G. perlatum*), the Red-chested Owlet (*G. tephronotum*), both 6½ inches, the Barred Owlet (*G. capense*), 8 inches, and the Chestnut-backed Owlet (*G. sjostedti*), 10 inches. All live south of the Sahara.

The Americans claim five pygmy species—the Northern Pygmy Owl (*G. gnoma*), 6 inches, of the Rocky Mountains; the Andean Pygmy Owl (*G. jardinii*), 5 to 5½ inches, ranging south to Peru; the Brazilian Pygmy Owl (*G. brazillianum*), 6½ inches, from Arizona into southern South America; and the Cuban (*G. siju*), 6½ inches and Least (*G. minutissimum*), 4½ to 5 inches, Pygmy Owls, both found from Mexico to Brazil.

Among the smallest of all the owls, the Elf Owl (*Micrathene whitneyi*), 5¼ inches, is a nocturnal insecteater native to the deserts of the southwestern United States and Mexico. It nests in woodpecker holes in giant cactuses.

Eurasian Pygmy Owl

Elf Owl; southwestern U.S. and Mexico.

Little Owl; Eurasia
and northern Africa.

Little Owls

The Little Owl (*Athene noctua*), 7 to 9 inches, ranges across
Europe, western and central Asia, northern Africa, and New
Zealand—where it has been introduced by man. It is common in agricultural countryside, hunting mostly at dawn
and dusk. Its undulating flight is like the woodpecker's.
The calls are variable but two rather plaintive similar notes
are most often heard. It lays two to five eggs. The Spotted
Owlet (*A. brama*), common from western India to Laos,
resembles the Little Owl but lives almost entirely on insects. The rare Forest Spotted Owlet (*A. blewitti*), 9 inches,
is a native of central and eastern India.

The Burrowing Owl (*Speotyto cunicularia*), 7 to 9 inches,
occurs from southwestern Canada to southern South America,
including Florida and some of the Caribbean Islands. It lives in
uncultivated flat country and prairies. It spends the day in
holes in the ground, emerging in the evening to hunt.

Tengmalm's or the Boreal Owl (*Aegolius funereus*), 10
inches, lives in coniferous woods in northern and eastern Europe, central Asia, Alaska and parts of Canada. It normally
hunts at night for rodents, small birds, frogs and insects. Its call
resembles the sound of dripping water. There are usually three

Tengmalm's or Boreal Owl;
Northern Hemisphere

Burrowing Owl;
Western Hemisphere

to six eggs laid in a hole in a tree. The brownly plumed Saw-whet Owl (*A. acadicus*), 6½ to 7½ inches, occurs from Alaska and Labrador to Mexico, exclusive of the southeastern United States. Completely nocturnal, it hunts chiefly for mice. The Unspotted Saw-whet Owl (*A. ridgwayi*), 7 inches, found from southern Mexico to Costa Rica, is similar, but lacks spots and bars on the wings and tail. The Buff-fronted Owl (*A. harrisii*), 7 to 8½ inches, occurs in Venezuela, Colombia and Ecuador, and in southeastern Brazil and northern Argentina.

147

Brown Hawk Owl; eastern Asia   New Guinea Hawk Owl

Hawk Owls

The Hawk Owl (*Surnia ulula*), 14 to 15 inches, inhabits
northern conifer and birch forests in the Old and New Worlds.
It hunts by daylight, and is able to kill birds its own size. It
breeds in holes in trees or in old nests.

Little is known about the New Guinea Hawk Owl (*Uroglaux dimorpha*), 10 to 11 inches, which has a long tail and
very fine barring below.

The Brown Hawk Owl (*Ninox scutulata*), 9 to 12 inches, is
found from Ceylon and Borneo to eastern Siberia. It hawks
large insects in flight and will also take mice, small birds and
shore crabs. A smaller bird, the Andaman Hawk Owl (*N.
affinis*), 9 inches, also occurs in the islands of southeast Asia.
The Philippine Hawk Owl (*N. philippensis*), 6 to 8 inches,
is another related species. Only one species has reached
the West, the Madagascar Hawk Owl (*N. superciliaris*), 9 to
11 inches. Celebes has two species—the Speckled Hawk Owl
(*N. punctulata*) and the Ochre-bellied Hawk Owl (*N. per-*

versa), both 8 to 10 inches long. The Mollucan Hawk Owl (*N. squampilia*), 10 to 14 inches, varies considerably in color. The Sooty-backed Hawk Owl (*N. theomacha*), 8 to 10 inches, is the small owl of lowland forests in New Guinea. The New Britain Hawk Owl (*N. odiosa*) is spotted white above like the last species. The New Ireland Hawk Owl (*N. solomonis*), 9 to 11 inches, also inhabits New Britain. The Solomon Islands Hawk Oil (*N. jacquinoti*), 8 to 10 inches, is a related species. Also in this area is the Admiralty Islands Hawk Owl (*N. meeki*), 9 to 12 inches. The Winking Owl (*N. connivens*), 10 to 18 inches, occurs on Halmerhera, eastern New Guinea and in Australia, except for the interior. Australian birds are the largest. The Boobook Owl (*N. novaeseelandiae*), 10 to 14 inches, occurs from the Moluccas to New Zealand and is very variable. The Rufous Owl (*N. rufa*), 17 to 18 inches, lives in lowland forests in New Guinea and northern Australia. The Powerful Owl (*N. strenua*), 20 to 23 inches, of southeastern Australia, is capable of killing rabbits and opossums.

Powerful Owl; Australia

Spectacled Owl;
Mexico to Argentina

Laughing and Tropical Wood Owls

The Laughing Owl (*Sceloglaux albifacies*), 13 to 15 inches, once common across New Zealand is now confined to South Island. It feeds on rodents, lizards, worms, and insects, and lays three eggs in holes in cliffs.

The Spectacled Owl (*Pulsatrix perspicillata*), 16 to 19 inches, is found from southern Mexico to Argentina. It lives in heavy tropical forest, preying on small mammals and insects, and lays two eggs

African Wood Owl; Africa
south of the Sahara

Laughing Owl; New Zealand

in a hole in a tree. Its call sounds like the tapping of a wood-pecker. The Rusty Barred Owl (*P. melanota*), 19 inches, has white eyebrows and is white below with brown bars. It occurs in Ecuador and Peru. In southern Brazil, the White-chinned Owl (*P. koeniswaldiana*), 17 inches, has yellow-orange on the eyebrows and chest, and a white barred tail.

The African Wood Owl (*Ciccaba woodfordii*), 11 to 13 inches, found over most of Africa south of the Sahara, frequents forest edges, woods and dense bush along the banks of streams. It hunts by night—at which time its loud three-syllabled call, with the accent on the last note, is frequently heard. One egg is the usual clutch. The Mottled Owl (*C. virgata*), 12 to 14 inches, occurs in mountain and tropical forests from Mexico to Argentina. It is dark brown with light spots above and white or tawny heavily streaked with deep brown below. The Black-and-White Owl (*C. nigrolineata*), 13 to 15 inches, found from southern Mexico to Ecuador, is white barred with black below extending to the upper back. The rest of it is black. The Black-Banded Owl (*C. huhula*), 16 inches, is an Amazonian forest species which is black throughout, barred with white.

Great Gray Owl;
N.A. and Eurasia

Wood Owls

The Rufous-banded Owl (*Ciccaba albitarsus*), 16 inches, occurs in the Andean forests from Venezuela to Ecuador.

The Great Gray Owl (*Strix nebulosa*), 27 inches, occurs in coniferous forests from Scandinavia, across central Siberia to parts of northern and western North America. It appears to be much larger than it is—owing to the volume of its feathers, which are insulation from the cold conditions under which it lives. It preys on squirrels, rats, mice and occasionally birds. The Barred Owl (*S. varia*), 17 to 19 inches, occurs from southern Canada to Honduras. It nests in an abandoned nest or in a tree cavity. The Spotted Owl (*S. occidentalis*), 16 to 18 inches, of western North America, is similar but is completely barred below, more heavily spotted above. Two South American wood owls are the Rufous-legged Owl (*S. rufipes*) and the Brazilian Owl (*S. hylophila*). The Tawny Owl (*S. aluco*), 13 to 16 inches, is common in wooded areas in Europe, across Asia to China, and in northwestern Africa. It favors mice, but rats or small rabbits are also taken. Where

Striped Owl; Mexico to Argentina

Barred Owl; North and Central America

rodents are scarce, birds form the main prey. Worms are eaten in wet weather, and frogs and insects occasionally. It lays two to four eggs in a hole in a tree or in a nest abandoned by large birds. Hume's Tawny Owl (*S. butleri*), 12 inches, known only from coastal Baluchistan, Palestine and Sinai, is buff in color. The Ural Owl (*S. uralensis*), of eastern Europe and central Asia, 24 inches in size, is buff, heavily streaked below. Southeast Asia has three species: The Mottled Wood Owl (*S. ocellata*), 16 to 18 inches, of India and Arakan, the Brown Wood Owl (*S. leptogrammica*), 13 to 20 inches, from India and Ceylon to Formosa and Java, and the Pagoda Owl (*S. seloputo*), 16 to 18 inches, from south Burma to Java.

The little-known Striped Owl (*Rhinoptynx clamator*), 13 to 15 inches, occurs from southern Mexico into Argentina.

Long-eared Owl; Eurasia and N.A.

Short-eared Owl; world-wide

Eared Owls

The Long-eared Owl (*Asio otus*), 13 to 14 inches, appears in Europe, central Asia, southern Canada and most of the United States. A woodland bird with unusually long wings, it lives on small mammals, birds up to the size of jays, and insects. It lays four or five eggs in an old squirrel's nest, abandoned bird's nests or on the ground. Its usual call is a low cooing moan uttered about every three seconds. The Long-eared Owl is decidedly a nocturnal and arboreal species and consequently is not often seen. The Abyssinian Long-eared Owl (*A. abyssinicus*), 14 to 16 inches, is darker and more heavily marked above than is the Long-eared. It occurs on Mount Kenya, the Ruwenzori range and the highlands of Ethiopia. The Madagascar Long-eared Owl (*A. madagascariensis*), 13 inches, is similar to the others but has orange-yellow in the plumage. The Stygian Owl (*A. stygius*) is found in forests—and often in mountains—from Mexico to northern Argentina. It also has prominent ear tufts. It is sooty above marked with orange, buff and white, and blotched and barred blackish below. The Short-eared Owl (*A. flammeus*), 14 to 16 inches, is found over most of the southern Arctic and temperate regions of the world. It hunts open country by day as well as by night and can often be identified in flight by the large, yellowish patch on each wing. It is a long-winged bird which glides low to the ground to surprise rodents or small birds. It makes a hollow in vegetation on the ground for its eggs—usually four to eight, but can lay up to fourteen. The African Marsh Owl (*A. capensis*), 12 to 15 inches, is another short-horned species, browner than the Short-eared. It lives mainly on large insects.

The Jamaican Owl (*Pseudoscops grammicus*), 11 to 13 inches, inhabits the Jamaican woodlands. The normal clutch is two eggs laid in a cavity in a tree.

The Fearful Owl (*Nesasio solomonensis*), 15 inches, lives in forests on Bougainville, Choiseul and Ysabel in the Solomon Islands. The feet and bill are exceptionally powerful for an owl of its size, and it is thought to kill oppossums and medium-sized birds. It is, however, one of the rarer species of owl.

Jamaican Owl

Fearful Owl; Solomon Islands

BOOKS TO READ

Eagles, Hawks and Falcons. Dean Amadon and Leslie Brown. McGraw-Hill, 1969.

Birds of Prey of the World. Mary Louise Grossman and John Hamlet. Potter, 1964.

Life Histories of North American Birds of Prey. A. C. Bent. (2 vol.) Dover, 1961.

The Art of Falconry. Emperor Frederick II of Hohenstaufen. (English translation of *De Arte Venandi cum Avibus*). Oxford University Press, 1959.

Hawks Aloft, The Story of Hawk Mountain. Maurice Broun. Dodd, Mead, 1949.

A Manual of Falconry. M. H. Woodford. Adam and Charles Black, 1960.

Eagles. Leslie Brown. London: Michael Joseph, 1955.

A Hawk for the Bush. J. G. Mavrogordato. London: H. F. and G. Witherby Ltd., 1960.

Pirates and Predators. R. Meinerzhagen. London: Oliver and Boyd, 1959.

The Art and Practice of Hawking. E. B. Michell. London: Holland Press, 1959.

The World of Birds. Roger Tory Peterson and James Fisher. Doubleday, 1964.

Fundamentals of Ornithology. Andrew J. Berger and Josselyn Van Tyne. John Wiley & Sons, 1959.

The Life of Birds. Joel C. Welty. Philadelphia: W. B. Saunders, 1962.

PLACES TO VISIT

Most major zoos have a good representative collection of living birds of prey on exhibit. The bigger natural history museums show stuffed specimens of hawklike birds and owls from all over the world. Regional museums will generally have some of the local birds of prey on display.

INDEX

Page numbers in bold type refer to illustrations.

Accipiter, genus 95
Aegolius, genus 46
Aegypius, genus 86
African Cuckoo Falcon 74
African Harrier Hawk **90**, 91
African Hobby 28
African Marsh Harrier 90
African Marsh Owl 155
African Pygmy Falcon 123
African Red-tailed Buzzard 104
African Sea Eagle 82, **83**
African Swallow-tailed Kite 78
African White-backed Vulture **86**, 88
African Wood Owl **150**, 151
Akun Eagle Owl **138**, 139
American Black Vulture 70, **71**
American Kestrel 39, **125**, 126
Andean Condor 39, 68, **69**
Aplomado Falcon 21, 130
Aquila, genus 110
Asio, genus 154
Athene, genus 146
Augur Buzzard 104
Australian Goshawk 99
Aviceda, genus 74
Ayres' Hawk Eagle 117

Bald Eagle 82, **82**
  spiralling display 16, **16**
Banded Harrier Eagle 92
Barbary Falcon 133, **133**
Bare-legged Owl 139
Barn Owl 134, **134**
Barred Forest Falcon 119
Barred Owl 152, **153**
Barred Owlet 145
Bat-eating Buzzard 75, **75**
  feeding methods 31
Bateleur **48**, 93
  nest **49**
  longevity 8
Bat Falcon **54**, 129
Bay Owl 135, **135**
Besra Sparrow Hawk 96
Bi-colored Hawk 95
Black and Chestnut Eagle 115
Black and White Goshawk 95
Black and White Hawk Eagle 116
Black Baza 31, 74, **74**
Black-breasted Kite 81
Black-collared Fishing Hawk 106, **107**
Black Eagle 112, **112**
Black-faced Hawk **105**, 106

Black Falcon 130
Black Hawk 107
Black Kite **27**, 79, **80**
Black-shouldered Kite 40, 79, **79**
Blakiston's Fish Owl 142
Blyth's Hawk Eagle 113
Bonelli's Eagle **116**, 117
Boobook Owl 149
Booted Eagle 20, 116
Bouvier's Fish Owl 143
Brahminy Kite 81, **81**
Brazilian Pygmy Owl 145
Broad-winged Hawk 21, 100
Broken claws 6, **6**
Brown Falcon **122**, 123
Brown Fish Owl **142**, 143
Brown Harrier Eagle **44**, 92
Brown Hawk Owl 148, **148**
Brown Wood Owl 153
Bubo, genus 139
Bumble foot 6, **6**
Burrowing Owl 146, **147**
Busarellus, genus 106
Butastur, genus 99
Buteo, genus 100
Buteogallus, genus 107
Buzzards 100-106

California Condor **4**, 68
Cape Eagle Owl 141
Cape Griffon Vulture 87
  nest **51**
Caracara 119
Cathartes, genus 71
Cayenne Kite 76
Changeable Hawk Eagle 113
Chanting Goshawk 94, **94**
Chelictinia, genus 78
Chimango Caracara 93
Chinese Goshawk 18, 97
Chondrohierax, genus 76
Ciccaba, genus 151
Cinereous Harrier 21, 91
Cinereous Vulture 86
Cinnamon Scops Owl 137
Circaetus, genus 92
Circus, genus 90
Collared Forest Falcon 118, **119**
Collared Scops Owl 137
Collared Sparrow Hawk 97
Common Buzzard 39, **101**, 103
Common Caracara **120**, 121
Common Kestral **33**, 34, 39, **53**, 124, **125**
Cooper's Hawk 21, 57, 95
Coragyps, genus 70
Crane Hawk 91
Crested Baza 74
Crested Eagle 108
Crested Goshawk 98
Crested Owl **138**, 139

Crested Serpent Eagle 92, **93**
Crowned Harpy Eagle **106**, 107
Crowned Hawk Eagle 10, 114, **115**
Cuckoo falcons 74

Daptrius, genus 119
Death, causes of 6
Desert Eagle Owl **140**, 141
Dickinson's Kestrel 127
Displays 14
Dryotriorchis, genus 93
Dusky Eagle Owl 141

Eagle Owl 141
Eggs 52, **53**
Egyptian Vulture **30**, **53**, **86**, 89, **89**
Elanoides, genus 78
Elanus, genus 70
Eleonora's Falcon 129
Elf Owl **5**, 145, **145**
Erythrotriorchis, genus 94
Eurasian Pygmy Owl 144, **145**
Eurasian Sparrow Hawk **26**, 57, 96
  sexual dimorphism 45, **45**
European Hobby 18, 129, **129**
Eutriorchis, genus 93

Falco, genus 123
Falconets 123
Falconry 56
Falcons 118-133
  killing method 30
Fearful Owl 155, **155**
Ferruginous Rough-legged Buzzard 102
Fielden's Falconet **122**, 123
Fish Owls 142-143
Fishing Eagles 84-85
Flammulated Owl 137
Food requirements 39
Forest Eagle Owl 141
Forest Falcons 118-120
Forster's Caracara 120, **120**
Fox Kestrel 123
Fraser's Eagle Owl 141

Gampsonyx, genus 79
Geranospiza, genus 91
Glaucidium, genus 144
Gold Coast Serpent Eagle 93, **93**
Golden Eagle **31**, 36, 39, 111, **111**
  juvenile development **41**
  nest **50**
  territory 10
  falconry 56, **56**
Goshawks 94-99
Grass Owl 134

Grasshopper Buzzard 99
Great Black Hawk 107, **107**
Great Eagle Buzzard 102
Great Eagle Owl 5, 22, **29**
31, 37, 53, 141
Great Gray Owl 21, 152,
152
Great Horned Owl **140**, 141
territory 10
Greater Spotted Eagle 18,
110
Greater Yellow-headed
Turkey Vulture **70**, 71
Gray Falcon 131, **131**
Gray Goshawk **97**, 98
Gray Hawk 100, **103**
Gray-headed Fishing Eagle
84, **84**
Gray Kestrel **124**, 126
Griffon **27**, 87, **87**
Gymnogyps, genus 68
Gypaetus, genus 89
Gypohierax, genus 85
Gyps, genus 87
Gyr Falcon **34, 59, 130,** 132

Haliaeetus, genus 82
Haliastur, genus 81
Hamirostra, genus 81
Harpagus, genus 75
Harpia, genus 108
Harpy Eagle 10, **27**, 108,
108
Harpyhaliaetus, genus 107
Harpyopsis, genus 108
Harrier eagles **27**, 92
killing methods 30
Harriers 90–91
hunting methods 23, 34,
91
Harris' Hawk 104, **104**
Hawk eagles 112–117
Hawk Owl **24**, 148
Hawks 94–107
hunting methods 35
Hen Harrier 91, **91**
Henicopernis, genus 77
Herpetotheres, genus 118
Heterospizias, genus 105
Hieraetus, genus 116
Himalayan Griffon **22**, 87
Honey Buzzard **76**, 77
Hooded Vulture **86**, 89
Hook-billed Kite 76

Icthyophaga, genus 84
Ictinaetus, genus 112
Ictinea, genus 77
Imperial Eagle 18, 110, **110**
Indian Black Vulture 38, 87
Indian White-backed
Vulture 88

Jamaican Owl 155, **155**
Jerdon's Baza 74
Jubula, genus 139
Jungle Owlet 145

Kaupifalco, genus 99
Kestrels 123–127
Ketupa, genus 142

King Vulture **68,** 70
Kites 74–81

Laggar Falcon 131
Lammergeyer 39, **88,** 89
Lanner Falcon 18, **22,** 56,
131, **131**
Large Barred Owlet 145
Laughing Falcon 118, **118**
Laughing Owl 150, **151**
Leptodon, genus 76
Lesser Fishing Eagle 84
Lesser Kestrel 18, 125
Lesser Spotted Eagle 18,
110
Letter-winged Kite 79
Leucopternis, genus 105
Levant Sparrow Hawk 98
Little Eagle 117
Little Falcon 128, **128**
Little Owl 146, **146**
in flight **25, 36**
Little Sparrow Hawk 97
Lizard Buzzard 99, **99**
Long-billed Vulture 88
Long-crested Hawk Eagle
116, **117**
Long-eared Owl 154, **154**
Longevity 8
Long-legged Buzzard 102
Long-tailed Hawk 94, **95**
Lophoaetus, genus 116
Lophoictinia, genus 81
Lophostrix, genus 139

Machaerhampus, genus 75
Madagascar Hawk Owl 148
Madagascar Sea Eagle 82
Madagascar Serpent Eagle
93
Malay Eagle Owl 141
Malay Fish Owl 142
Maned Owl 139, **139**
Marsh Harrier 34, 90, **90**
Martial Eagle 36, **114,** 115
Masked Owl 135, **135**
Megatriorchis, genus 94
Melierax, genus 94
Merlin 21, **126,** 127
Micrastur, genus 118
Microhierax, genus 123
Migration 18
Milky Eagle Owl 141
Milvago, genus 121
Milvus, genus 79
Mississippi Kite 78
Monkey-eating Eagle 109,
109
Montagu's Harrier **23,** 91
Morphnus, genus 108
Mottled Owl 151
Mottled Wood Owl 153
Mountain Buzzard 103
Mountain Caracara 120
Mountain Hawk Eagle **32,**
112
Mountain Scops Owl 136

Nankeen Kestrel 125
Necrosyrtes, genus 89
Neophron, genus 89
Nesasio, genus 155

Nests 50
New Guinea Harpy Eagle
108
New Guinea Hawk Owl
148, **148**
New Zealand Falcon 130
Ninox, genus 148
Northern Goshawk 18, 21,
47, 58, 95, **96**
Northern Pygmy Owl 145
Nyctea, genus 143

Orange-breasted Falcon
132
Oriental Hobby 128
Ornate Hawk Eagle **113,**
114
Oroaetus, genus 115
Osprey 21, **27,** 73, **73**
at nest **51**
Otus, genus 136
Ovampo Sparrow Hawk 96
Owls 134–155
feeding methods 31
hunting methods 36

Pagoda Owl 153
Pallas's Sea Eagle 82
Pallid Harrier 91
Pandion, genus 73
Parabuteo, genus 104
Peale's Falcon **132,** 133
Pearl Kite 79
Pearl Spotted Owlet 145
Pellets 42
Pel's Fish Owl **29,** 143, **143**
Peregrine Falcon 18, **29,** 39
46, 58, 133, **133**
hunting methods 24
Pernis, genus 77
Pets 62
accommodation for 65
diet for 66
Phalcoboenus, genus 120
Philippine Eagle Owl 142
Philippine Hawk Eagle 113
Philippine Serpent Eagle 92
Pied Harrier 90
Pithecophaga, genus 109
Plumbeous Kite 21, 77
Polemaetus, genus 115
Poliohierax, genus 123
Polyboroides, genus 91
Polyborus, genus 122
Powerful Owl 149, **149**
Prairie Falcon 131
Pseudoscops, genus 155
Pulsatrix, genus 150
Pygmy Owls 144

Rajah Scops Owl 138
Red-backed Buzzard 100
pellets 42
Reddish Scops Owl 136
Red-footed Falcon 18, 127
migration 18
Red Goshawk 94, **94**
Red-headed Merlin 57, 127,
127
Red-headed Turkey
Vulture 21, **70,** 71
Red Kite 80, **80**
Red-shouldered Hawk 100

Red-tailed Hawk 21, **101**
102
Red-thighed Falconet **4,**
39, 121
Red-throated Caracara
119, **121**
Rhinoptynx, genus 153
Roadside Hawk 100, **103**
Rostrahamus, genus 76
Rough-legged Hawk **100,**
102
Rufous-bellied Hawk
Eagle 117
Rufous-breasted Sparrow
Hawk 96, **98**
Rufous Fish Owl 143
Rufous Owl 149
Rufous-winged Buzzard 99
Ruppell's Griffon **86,** 88
Russet Scops Owl 137

Sagittarius, genus 72
Saker Falcon 18, **130,** 131
falconry 56
Sanford's Sea Eagle 82
Sarcogyps, genus 87
Sarcohamphus, genus 70
Savannah Hawk 105
Saw-whet Owl **12,** 147
Sceloglaux, genus 150
Scops Owl **29,** 136, **136**
pellet from 36
Scotopelia, genus 143
Screech Owl **137,** 138
Sea Eagles 92–93
Serpent Eagles 92–93
Sharp-skinnned Hawk 21,
96
Shed **64,** 65
Shikra **23,** 57, 97
Short-eared Owl 25, 154,
154
Short-tailed Buzzard 100
Short-toed Eagle 18, 39,
92, **92**

Snail Kite 76, **77**
Snowy Owl 21, **28,** 143, **144**
Sociable Vulture **30, 86,** 87
Solitary Harpy 107
Sooty Falcon 129
Southern Banded Harrier
Eagle 92
Sparrow Hawks 96–98
Spectacled Owl 150, **150**
Speotyto, genus 146
Spilornis, genus 92
Spix Screech Owl 39, 138
Spizaetus, genus 112
Spizapteryx, genus 123
Spizastur, genus 116
Spotted Eagle Owl 17, 141,
144
Spotted Harrier 90
Spotted Owl 152
Spotted Owlet 146
Spot-winged Falcon **122,**
123
Square-tailed Kite 81
Steller's Sea Eagle 39, 82,
83
Stephanoaetus, genus 114
Steppe Eagle 110
Striped Owl 153, **153**
Strix, genus 152
Stygian Owl 154
Surnia, genus 148
Swainson's Buzzard 103
Swallow-tailed Kite 78, **78**

Taita Falcon 132
Tawny Eagle 110
Tawny Fish Owl 142
Tawny Owl 29, **67,** 152
pellet 42
egg **53**
Tengmalm's Owl 146, **147**
Terathopius, genus 93
Territory 10
Tiny Hawk 96
Torgos, genus 87
Trigonoceps, genus 86
Tyrant Hawk Eagle 114

Tyto genus 134

Upland Buzzard 102
Ural Owl 153
Uroglaux, genus 148
Urotriorchis, genus 94

Variable Goshawk **97,** 98
Verreaux's Eagle **11, 35,**
111
territory 10
Vultur, genus 68
Vultures 68–71, 86–89
feeding methods 30
hunting methods 33
Vulturine Fish Eagle 85, **85**

Wahlberg's Eagle 117
Wedge-tailed Eagle 111,
111
Whiskered Screech Owl
138
Whistling Kite or Eagle 81
White-bellied Sea Eagle 82
White-eyed Buzzard 99
White-eyed Kestrel 123
White-faced Scops Owl
136, 137
White Hawk **105,** 106
White-headed Falconet **38,**
123
White-headed Vulture 86,
86
White-tailed Hawk 101, **102**
White-tailed Kite 79
White-tailed Sea Eagle 18,
53, 82
Winking Owl 149

Yellow-headed Caracara
121, **121**
Yellow-throated Caracara
119

Zone-tailed Buzzard 104

OTHER TITLES IN THE SERIES

The GROSSET ALL-COLOR GUIDES provide a library of authoritative information for readers of all ages. Each comprehensive text with its specially designed illustrations yields a unique insight into a particular area of man's interests and culture.

NOW AVAILABLE

PREHISTORIC ANIMALS
BIRD BEHAVIOR
WILD CATS
FOSSIL MAN
PORCELAIN
MILITARY UNIFORMS, 1686–1918
BIRDS OF PREY
FLOWER ARRANGING
MICROSCOPES & MICROSCOPIC LIFE
THE PLANT KINGDOM
ROCKETS & MISSILES
FLAGS OF THE WORLD
ATOMIC ENERGY
WEATHER & WEATHER FORECASTING
TRAINS
SAILING SHIPS & SAILING CRAFT
ELECTRONICS
MYTHS & LEGENDS OF ANCIENT GREECE
CATS, HISTORY—CARE—BREEDS
DISCOVERY OF AFRICA
HORSES & PONIES
FISHES OF THE WORLD
ASTRONOMY
SNAKES OF THE WORLD
DOGS, SELECTION—CARE—TRAINING

SOON TO BE PUBLISHED

GUNS
EXPLORING THE PLANETS
DISCOVERY OF THE AMERICAN WEST
MAMMALS OF THE WORLD
ANIMALS OF AUSTRALIA & NEW ZEALAND
JEWELRY
WARSHIPS
TREES OF THE WORLD
COMPUTERS AT WORK
ARCHITECTURE
MONKEYS & APES
THE ANIMAL KINGDOM
DISCOVERY OF NORTH AMERICA
ENGLISH VICTORIANA
NATURAL HISTORY COLLECTING
MYTHS & LEGENDS OF ANCIENT EGYPT
THE HUMAN BODY
TROPICAL AQUARIUM FISHES
AFRICAN ANIMALS
VETERAN & VINTAGE CARS
MYTHS & LEGENDS OF THE SOUTH SEAS
MYTHS & LEGENDS OF ANCIENT ROME
MYTHS & LEGENDS OF ANCIENT INDIA
ARMS & ARMOR
DISCOVERY OF SOUTH AMERICA